MY DAY -TO- DAY HOLIDAY BOOK

AGE 5-8

WRITTEN BY
Sally Emerson

ILLUSTRATED BY
Sally Townsend

A Piccolo Original
PAN MACMILLAN
CHILDREN'S BOOKS

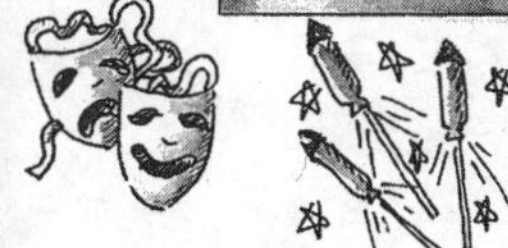

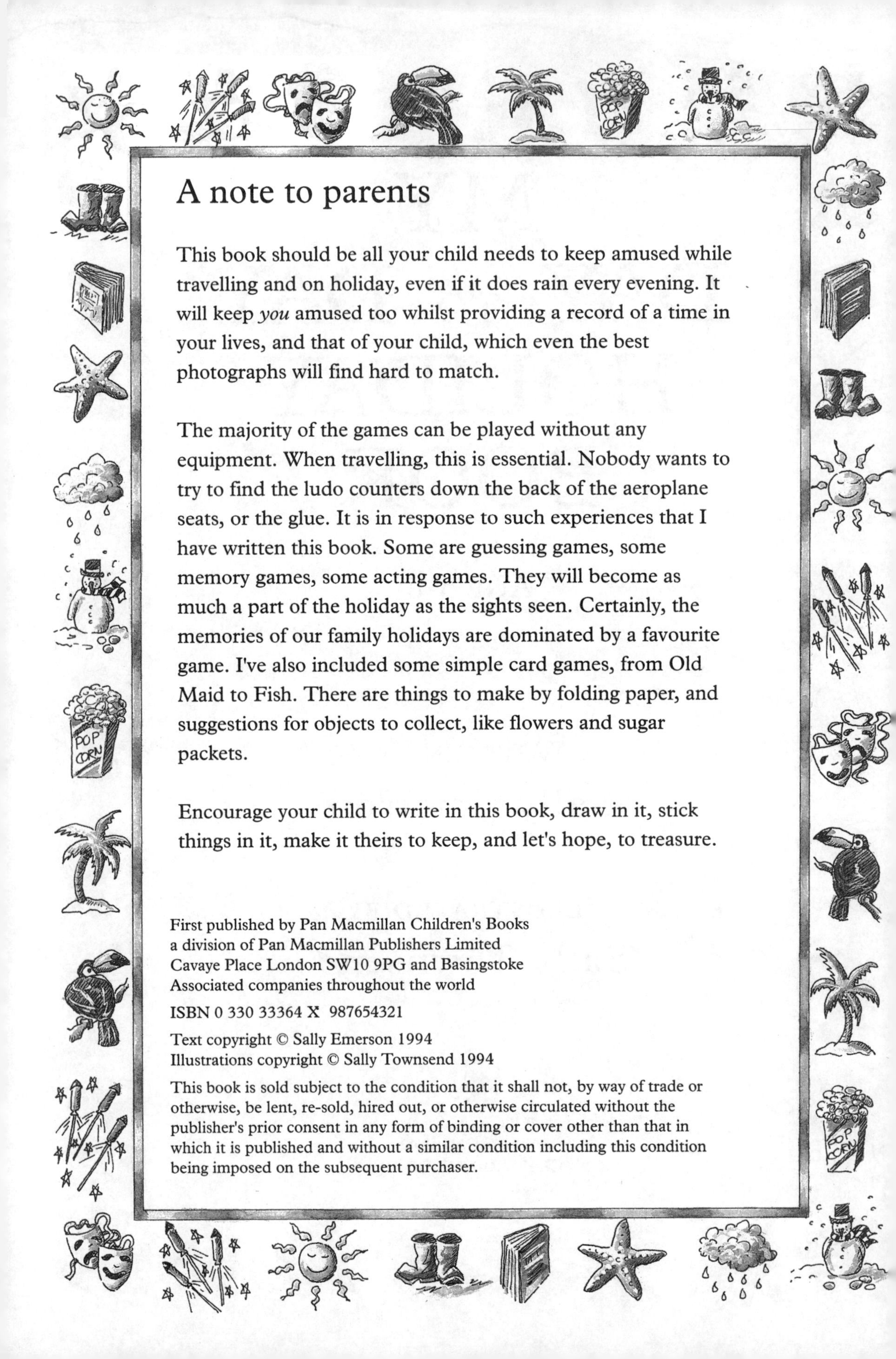

A note to parents

This book should be all your child needs to keep amused while travelling and on holiday, even if it does rain every evening. It will keep *you* amused too whilst providing a record of a time in your lives, and that of your child, which even the best photographs will find hard to match.

The majority of the games can be played without any equipment. When travelling, this is essential. Nobody wants to try to find the ludo counters down the back of the aeroplane seats, or the glue. It is in response to such experiences that I have written this book. Some are guessing games, some memory games, some acting games. They will become as much a part of the holiday as the sights seen. Certainly, the memories of our family holidays are dominated by a favourite game. I've also included some simple card games, from Old Maid to Fish. There are things to make by folding paper, and suggestions for objects to collect, like flowers and sugar packets.

Encourage your child to write in this book, draw in it, stick things in it, make it theirs to keep, and let's hope, to treasure.

First published by Pan Macmillan Children's Books
a division of Pan Macmillan Publishers Limited
Cavaye Place London SW10 9PG and Basingstoke
Associated companies throughout the world

ISBN 0 330 33364 X 987654321

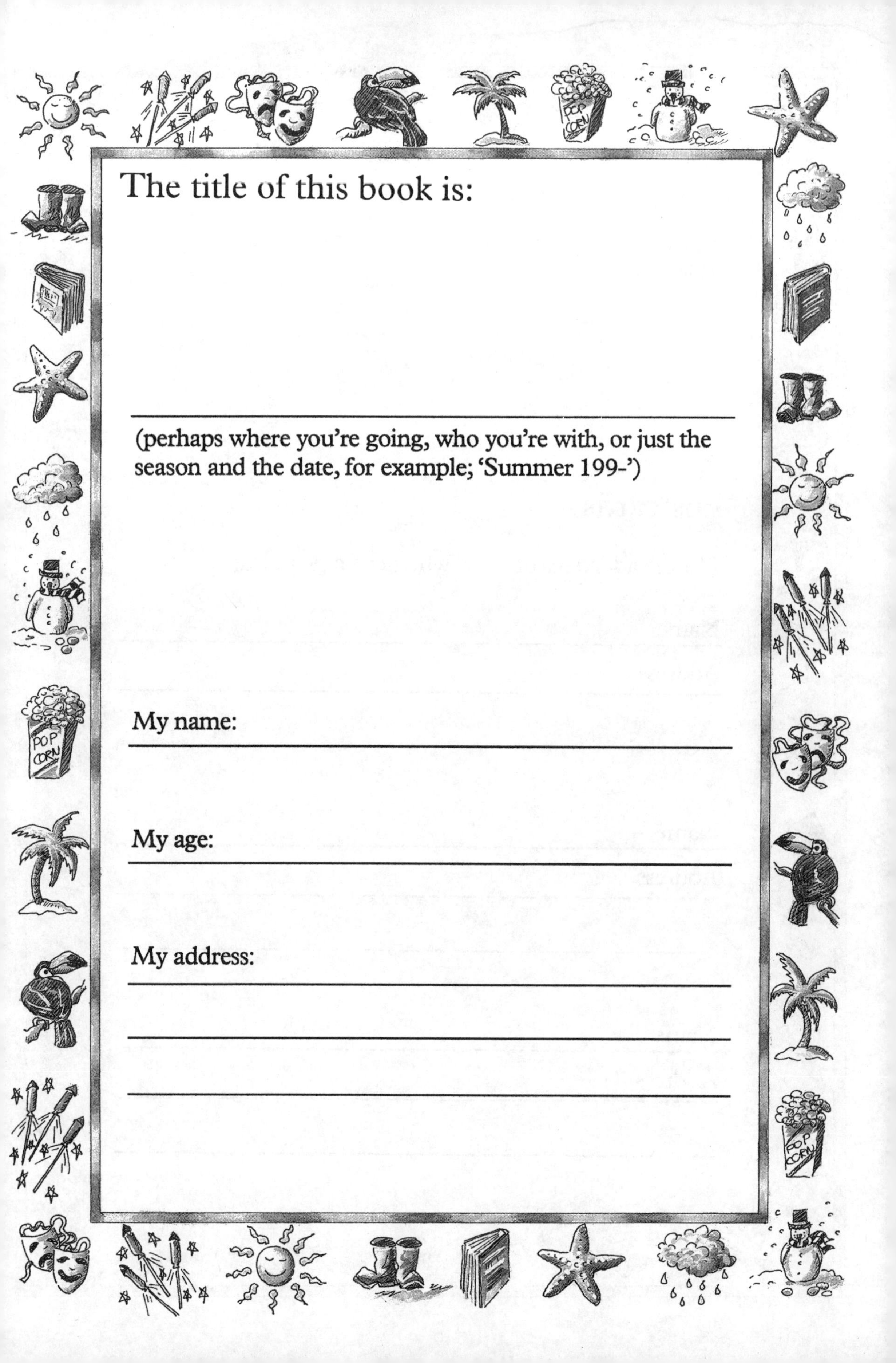

The title of this book is:

___

(perhaps where you're going, who you're with, or just the season and the date, for example; 'Summer 199-')

My name:

___

My age:

___

My address:

___

___

___

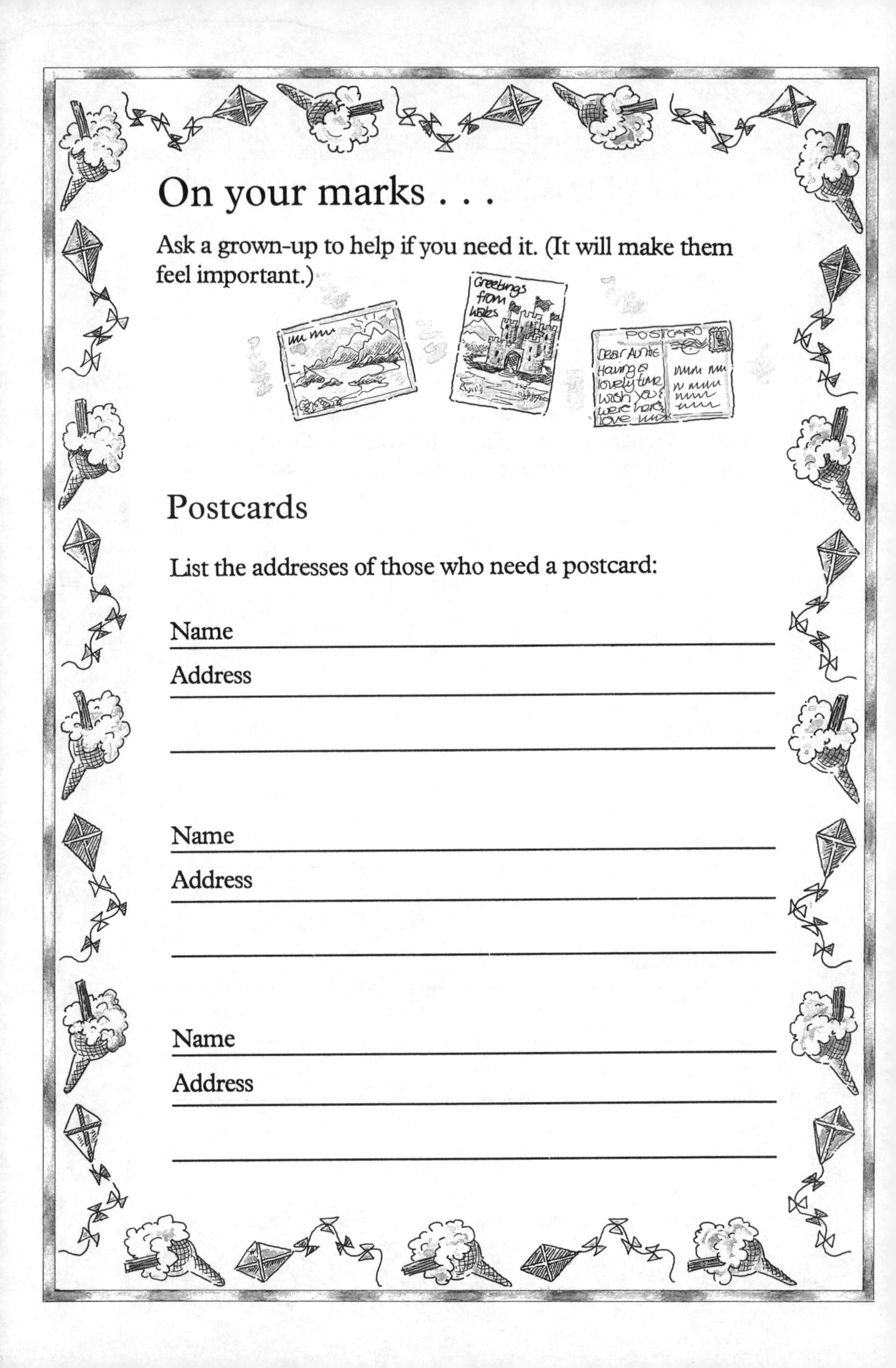

On your marks . . .

Ask a grown-up to help if you need it. (It will make them feel important.)

Postcards

List the addresses of those who need a postcard:

Name ______________________________

Address ______________________________

____

Name ______________________________

Address ______________________________

____

Name ______________________________

Address ______________________________

____

Holiday money you have to spend

Keep a record here of how much you spend and what you spent it on.

What you've bought	How much it cost

Presents

Who'll receive a present	Approximate cost

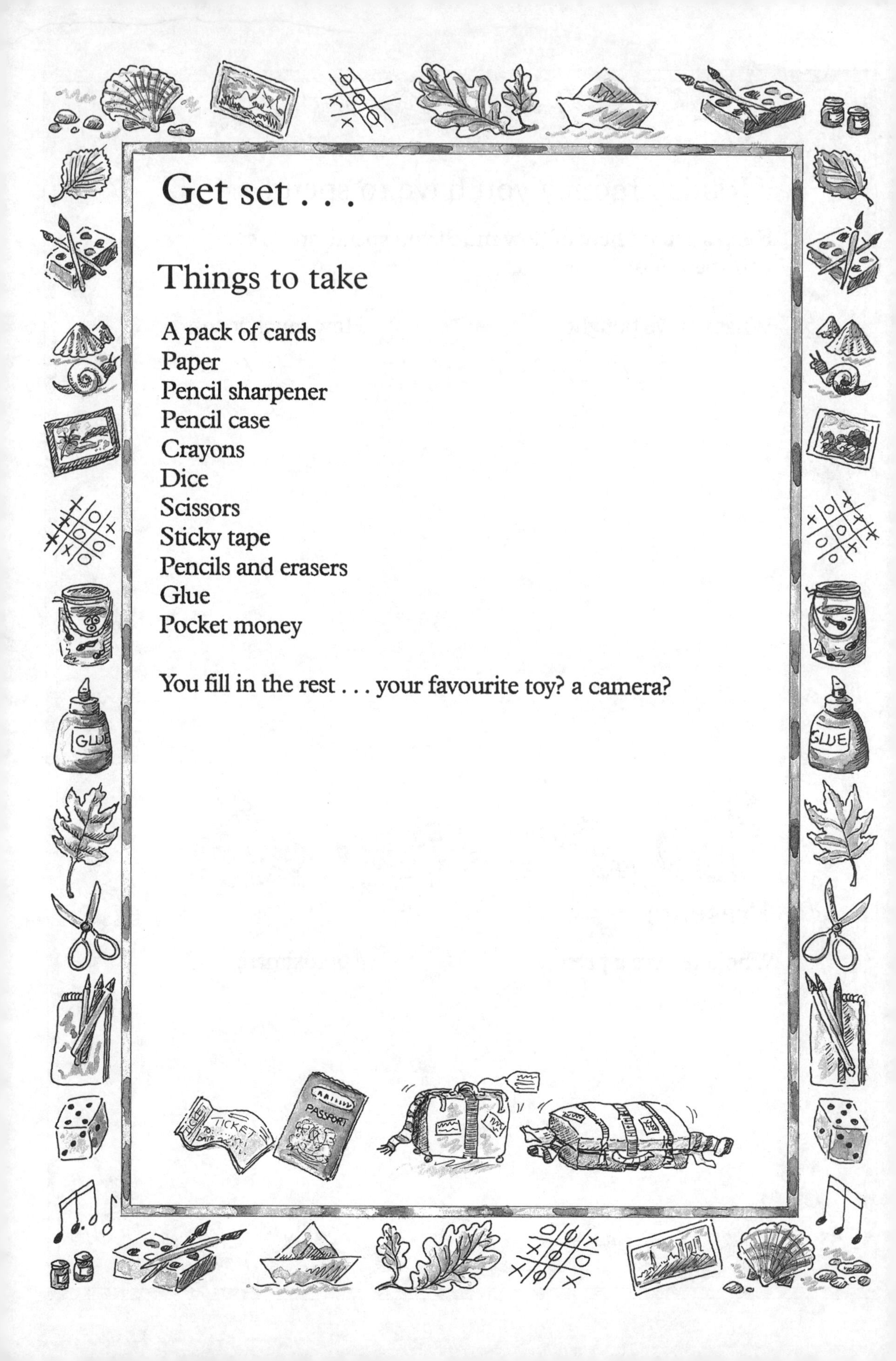

Get set . . .

Things to take

A pack of cards
Paper
Pencil sharpener
Pencil case
Crayons
Dice
Scissors
Sticky tape
Pencils and erasers
Glue
Pocket money

You fill in the rest . . . your favourite toy? a camera?

Books to read

Clothes to pack

Don't forget to telephone your friends to say goodbye - and to remind your parents to water the plants, cancel the papers and tell the milkman not to call.

Go!

Day 1

Date:

Place:

Weather:

Today we:

Most interesting/funniest time:

Bag puppets

If you're in a plane, try making puppets out of sick bags in the seat pockets. Draw on faces and get the paper bag puppets talking. You could act out a play with them.

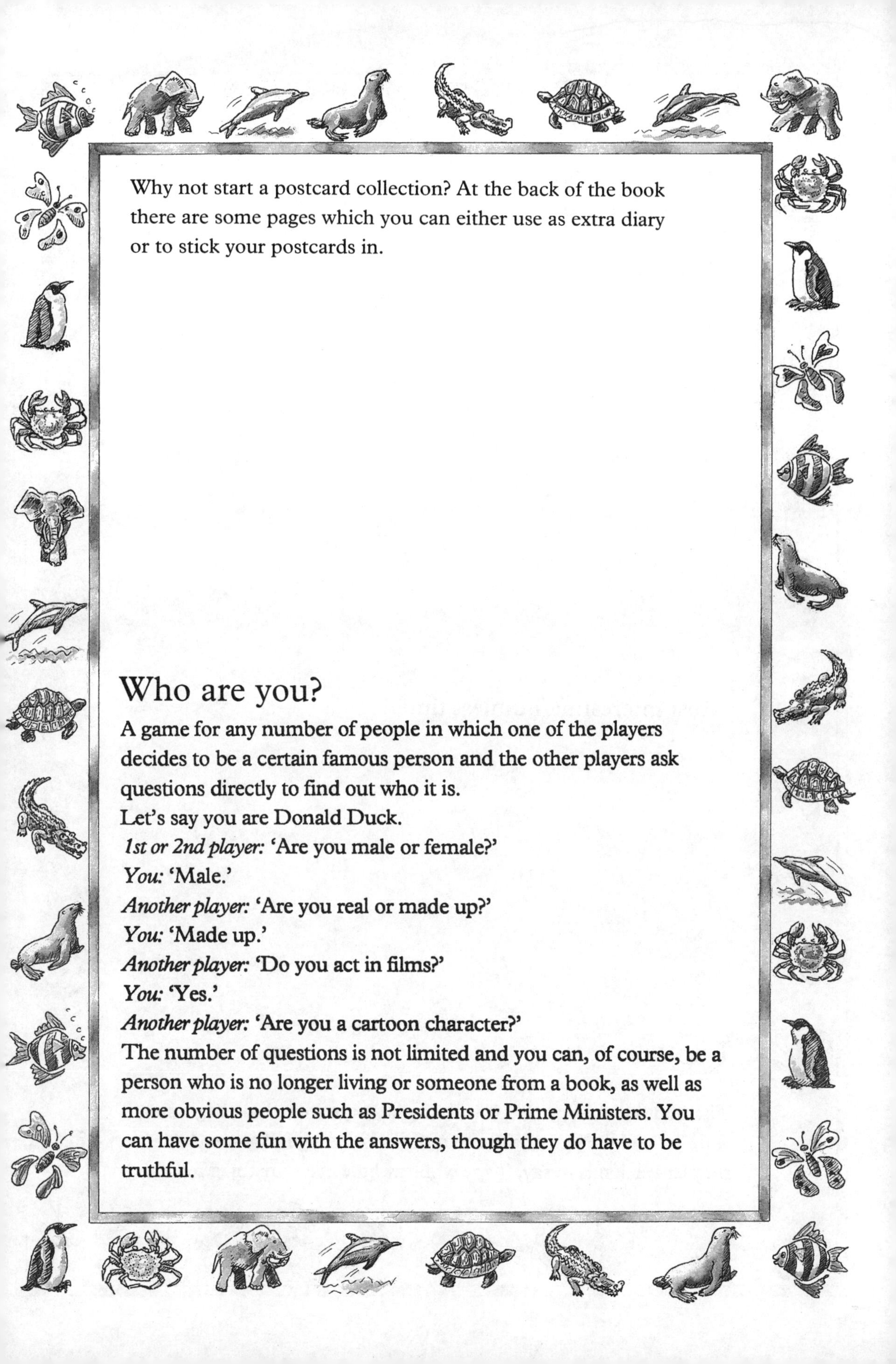

Why not start a postcard collection? At the back of the book there are some pages which you can either use as extra diary or to stick your postcards in.

Who are you?

A game for any number of people in which one of the players decides to be a certain famous person and the other players ask questions directly to find out who it is.

Let's say you are Donald Duck.

1st or 2nd player: 'Are you male or female?'

You: 'Male.'

Another player: 'Are you real or made up?'

You: 'Made up.'

Another player: 'Do you act in films?'

You: 'Yes.'

Another player: 'Are you a cartoon character?'

The number of questions is not limited and you can, of course, be a person who is no longer living or someone from a book, as well as more obvious people such as Presidents or Prime Ministers. You can have some fun with the answers, though they do have to be truthful.

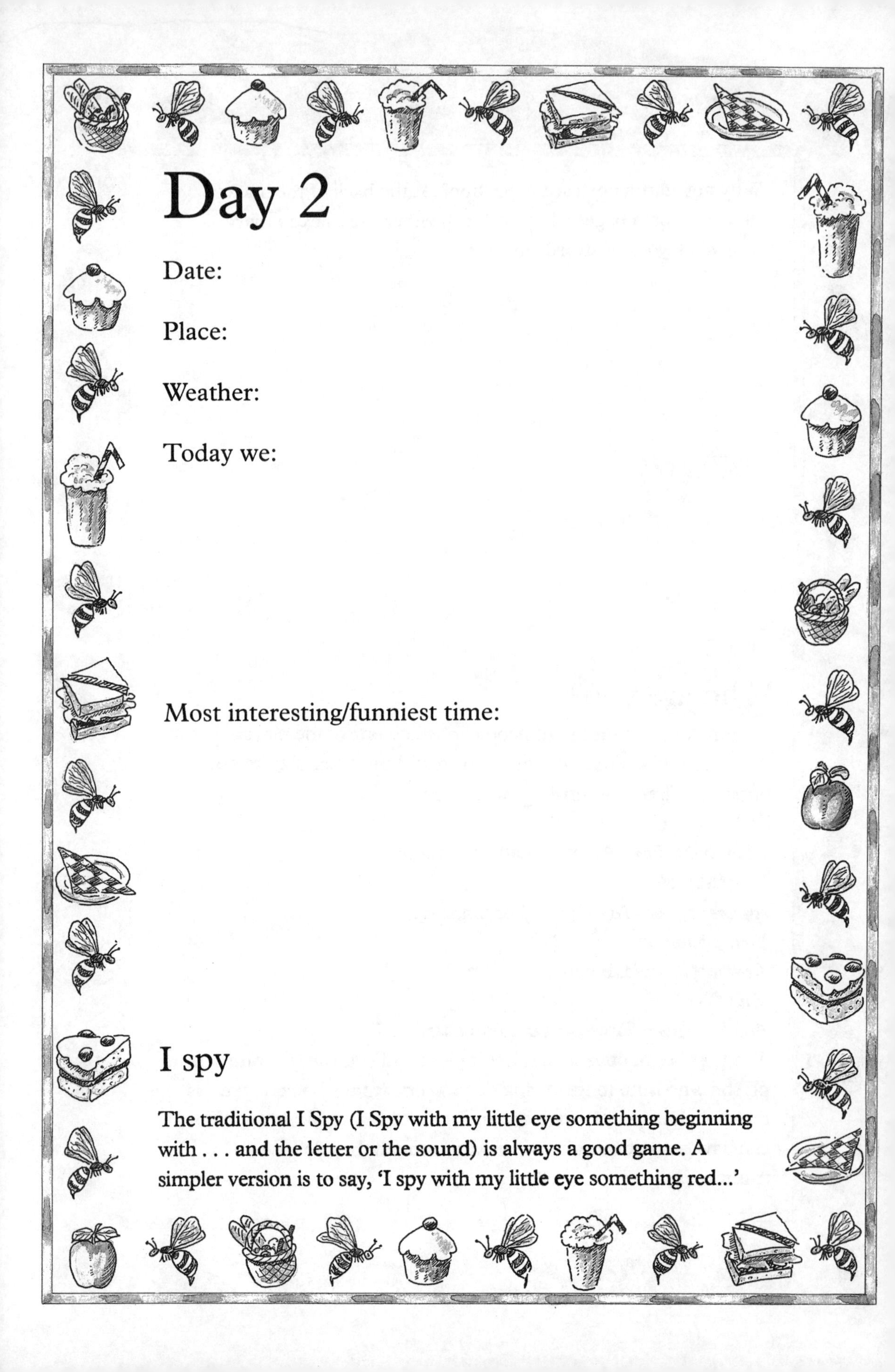

Day 2

Date:

Place:

Weather:

Today we:

Most interesting/funniest time:

I spy

The traditional I Spy (I Spy with my little eye something beginning with . . . and the letter or the sound) is always a good game. A simpler version is to say, 'I spy with my little eye something red...'

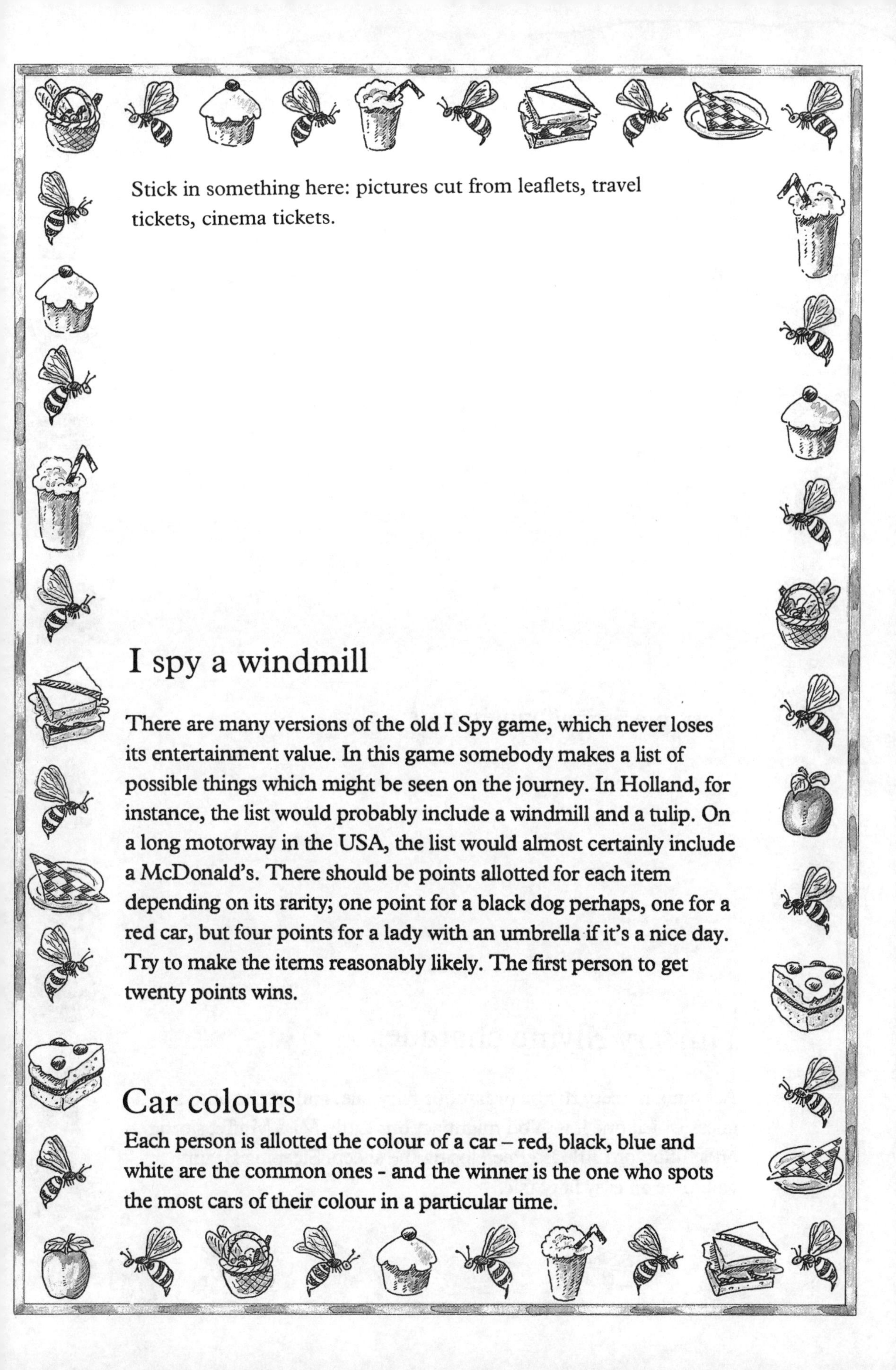

Stick in something here: pictures cut from leaflets, travel tickets, cinema tickets.

I spy a windmill

There are many versions of the old I Spy game, which never loses its entertainment value. In this game somebody makes a list of possible things which might be seen on the journey. In Holland, for instance, the list would probably include a windmill and a tulip. On a long motorway in the USA, the list would almost certainly include a McDonald's. There should be points allotted for each item depending on its rarity; one point for a black dog perhaps, one for a red car, but four points for a lady with an umbrella if it's a nice day. Try to make the items reasonably likely. The first person to get twenty points wins.

Car colours

Each person is allotted the colour of a car – red, black, blue and white are the common ones - and the winner is the one who spots the most cars of their colour in a particular time.

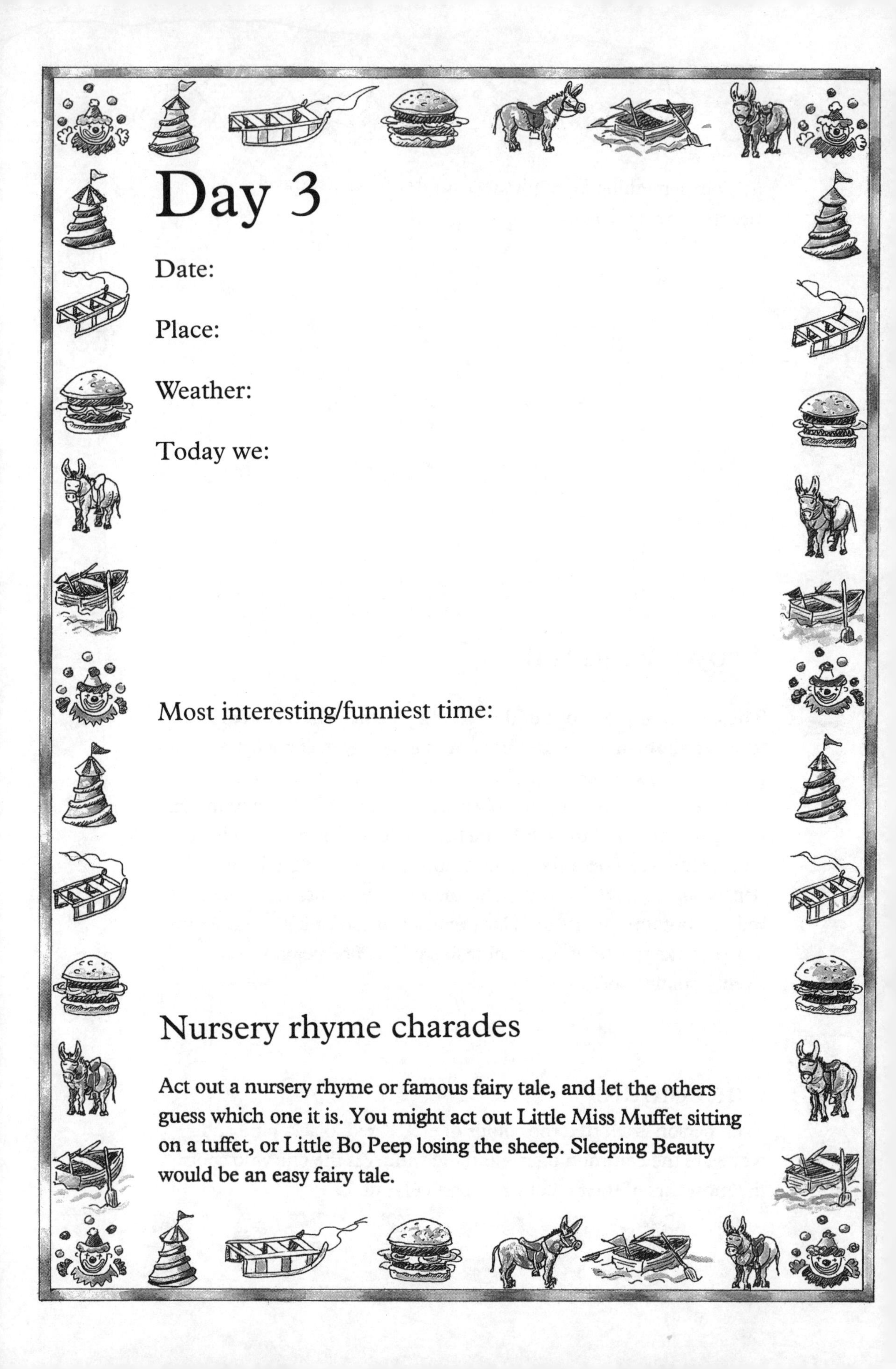

Day 3

Date:

Place:

Weather:

Today we:

Most interesting/funniest time:

Nursery rhyme charades

Act out a nursery rhyme or famous fairy tale, and let the others guess which one it is. You might act out Little Miss Muffet sitting on a tuffet, or Little Bo Peep losing the sheep. Sleeping Beauty would be an easy fairy tale.

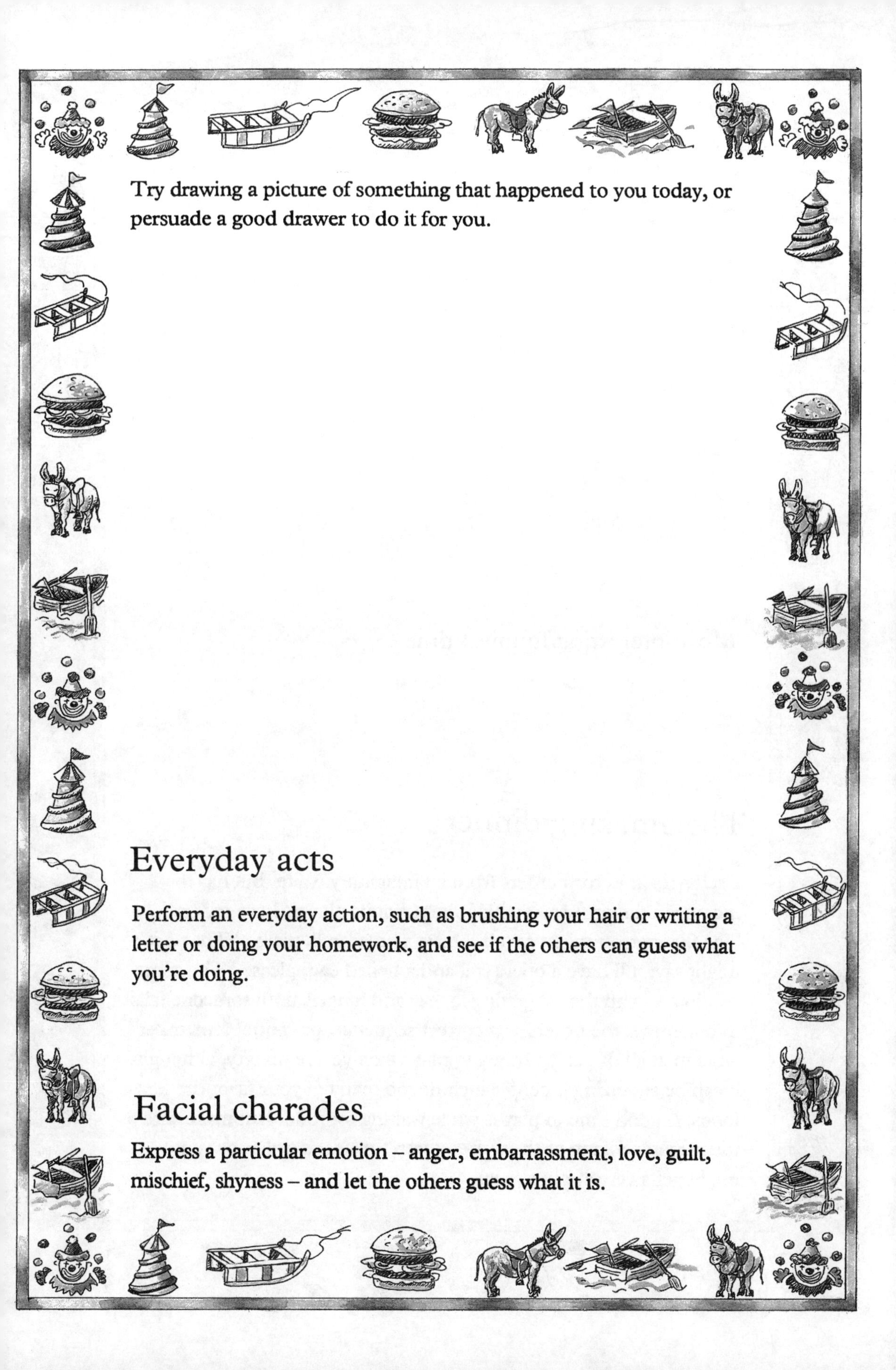

Try drawing a picture of something that happened to you today, or persuade a good drawer to do it for you.

Everyday acts

Perform an everyday action, such as brushing your hair or writing a letter or doing your homework, and see if the others can guess what you're doing.

Facial charades

Express a particular emotion – anger, embarrassment, love, guilt, mischief, shyness – and let the others guess what it is.

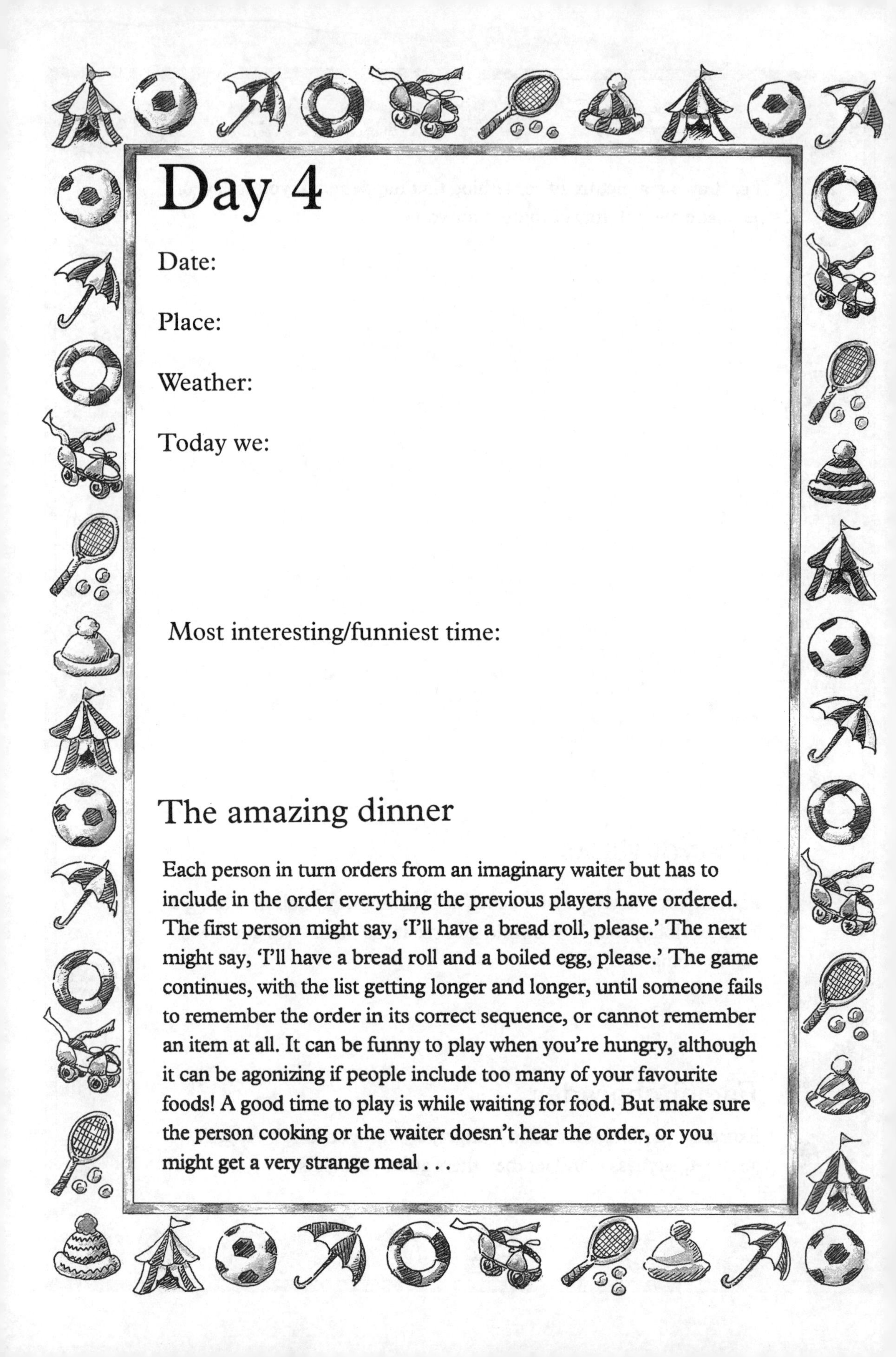

Day 4

Date:

Place:

Weather:

Today we:

Most interesting/funniest time:

The amazing dinner

Each person in turn orders from an imaginary waiter but has to include in the order everything the previous players have ordered. The first person might say, 'I'll have a bread roll, please.' The next might say, 'I'll have a bread roll and a boiled egg, please.' The game continues, with the list getting longer and longer, until someone fails to remember the order in its correct sequence, or cannot remember an item at all. It can be funny to play when you're hungry, although it can be agonizing if people include too many of your favourite foods! A good time to play is while waiting for food. But make sure the person cooking or the waiter doesn't hear the order, or you might get a very strange meal . . .

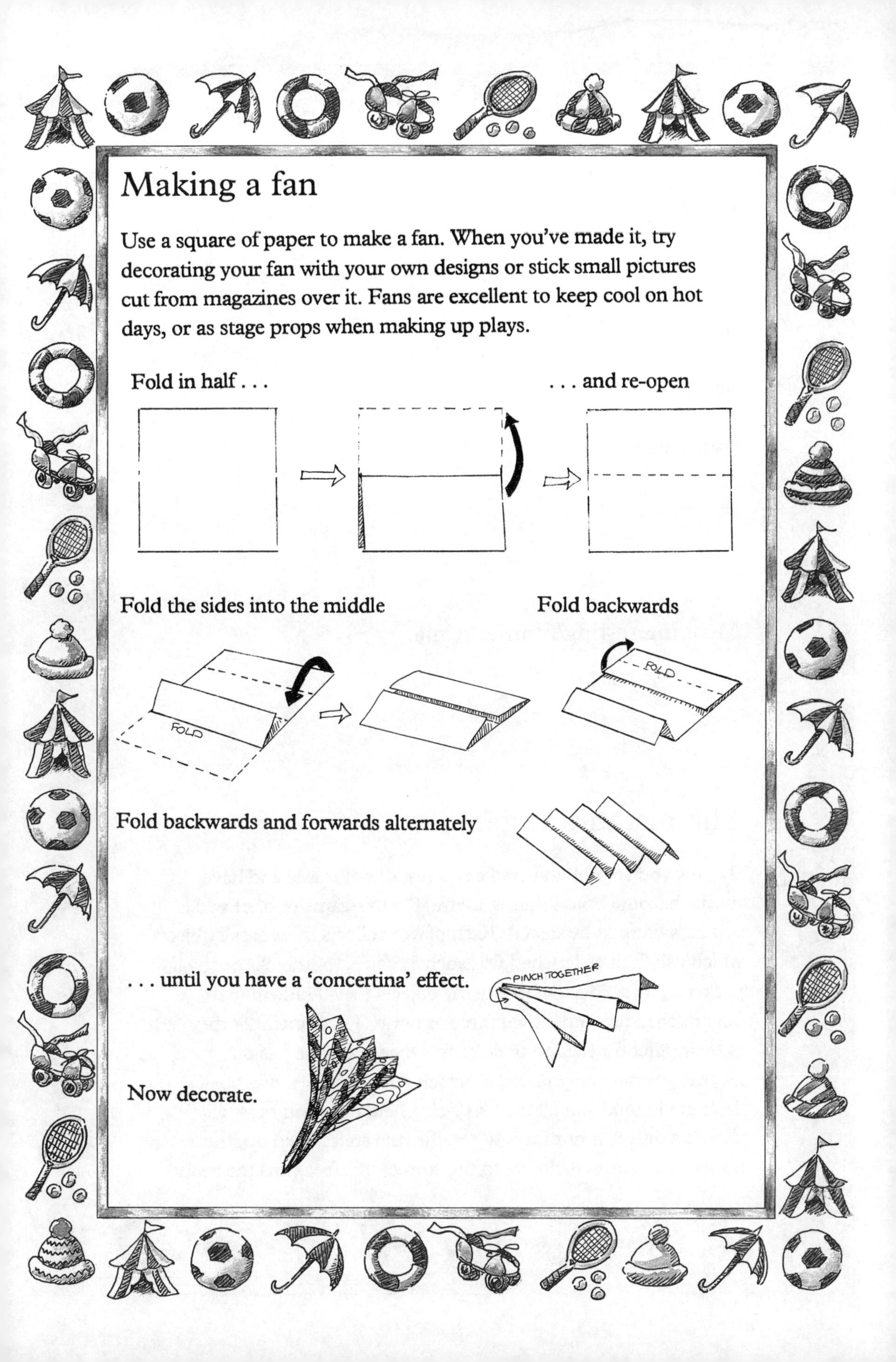

Making a fan

Use a square of paper to make a fan. When you've made it, try decorating your fan with your own designs or stick small pictures cut from magazines over it. Fans are excellent to keep cool on hot days, or as stage props when making up plays.

Fold in half . . .

. . . and re-open

Fold the sides into the middle

Fold backwards

Fold backwards and forwards alternately

. . . until you have a 'concertina' effect.

Now decorate.

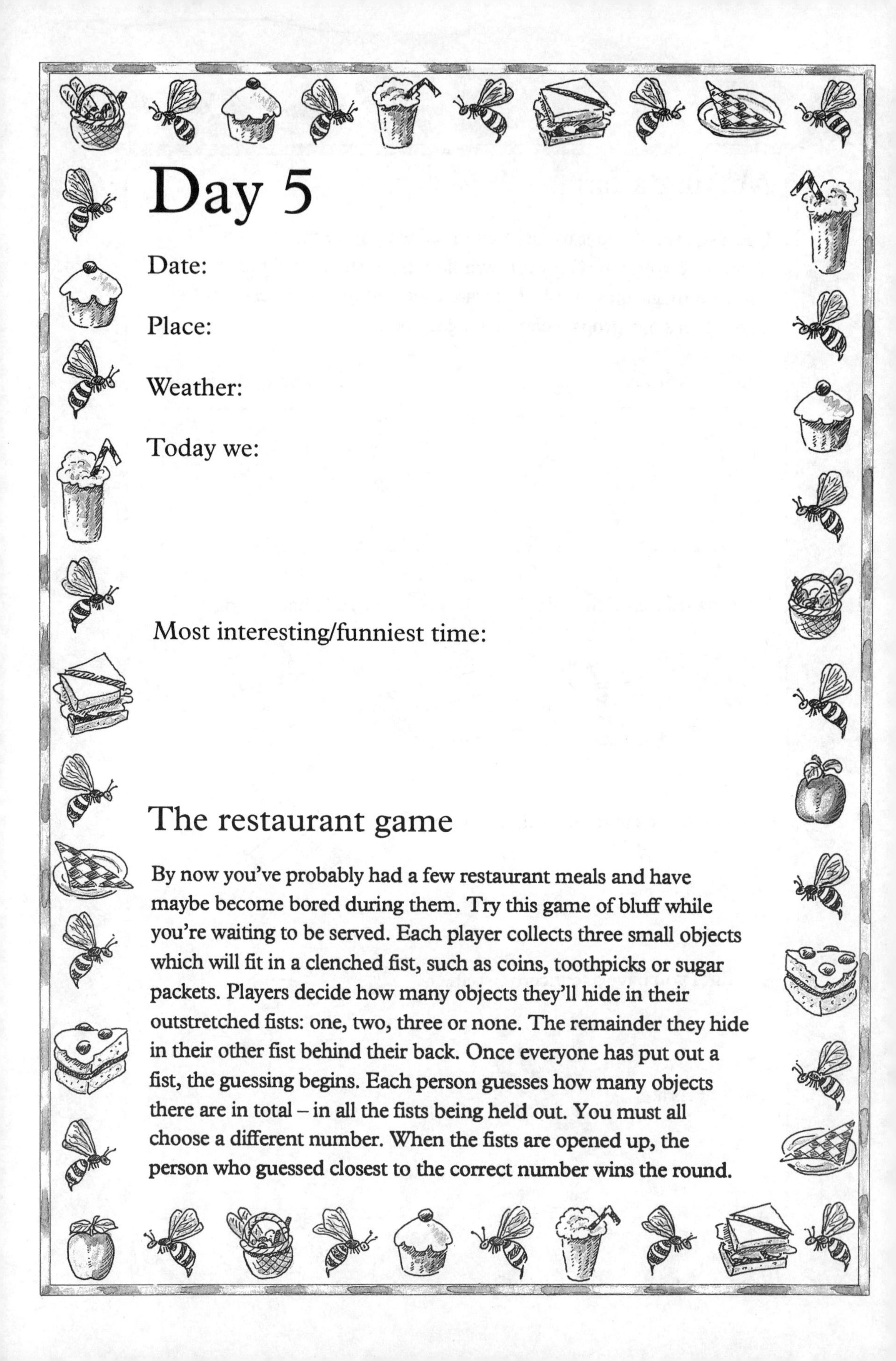

Day 5

Date:

Place:

Weather:

Today we:

Most interesting/funniest time:

The restaurant game

By now you've probably had a few restaurant meals and have maybe become bored during them. Try this game of bluff while you're waiting to be served. Each player collects three small objects which will fit in a clenched fist, such as coins, toothpicks or sugar packets. Players decide how many objects they'll hide in their outstretched fists: one, two, three or none. The remainder they hide in their other fist behind their back. Once everyone has put out a fist, the guessing begins. Each person guesses how many objects there are in total – in all the fists being held out. You must all choose a different number. When the fists are opened up, the person who guessed closest to the correct number wins the round.

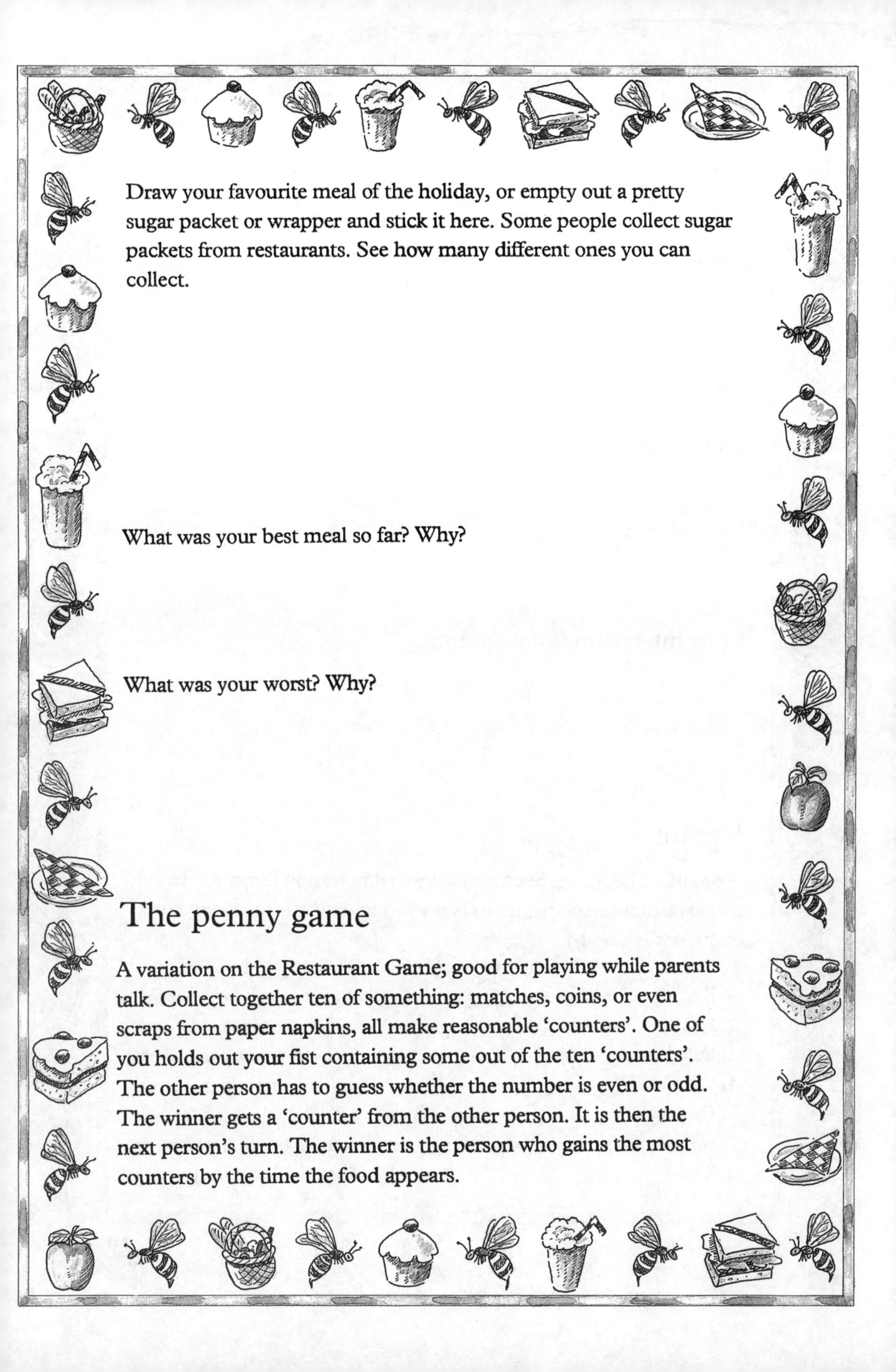

Draw your favourite meal of the holiday, or empty out a pretty sugar packet or wrapper and stick it here. Some people collect sugar packets from restaurants. See how many different ones you can collect.

What was your best meal so far? Why?

What was your worst? Why?

The penny game

A variation on the Restaurant Game; good for playing while parents talk. Collect together ten of something: matches, coins, or even scraps from paper napkins, all make reasonable 'counters'. One of you holds out your fist containing some out of the ten 'counters'. The other person has to guess whether the number is even or odd. The winner gets a 'counter' from the other person. It is then the next person's turn. The winner is the person who gains the most counters by the time the food appears.

Day 6

Date:

Place:

Weather:

Today we:

Most interesting/funniest time:

Beetle

A popular dice game. Each player takes it in turn to throw a dice and each number on the dice allows you to draw the following bits of the beetle's body:

1. Body
2. Head
3. One leg
4. One eye
5. One feeler (or antenna)
6. Tail

To start, a player must throw a 'one' to give him or her the body. The feelers or eyes can only be drawn when the head is on. The winner is, of course, the first person to draw a whole beetle.

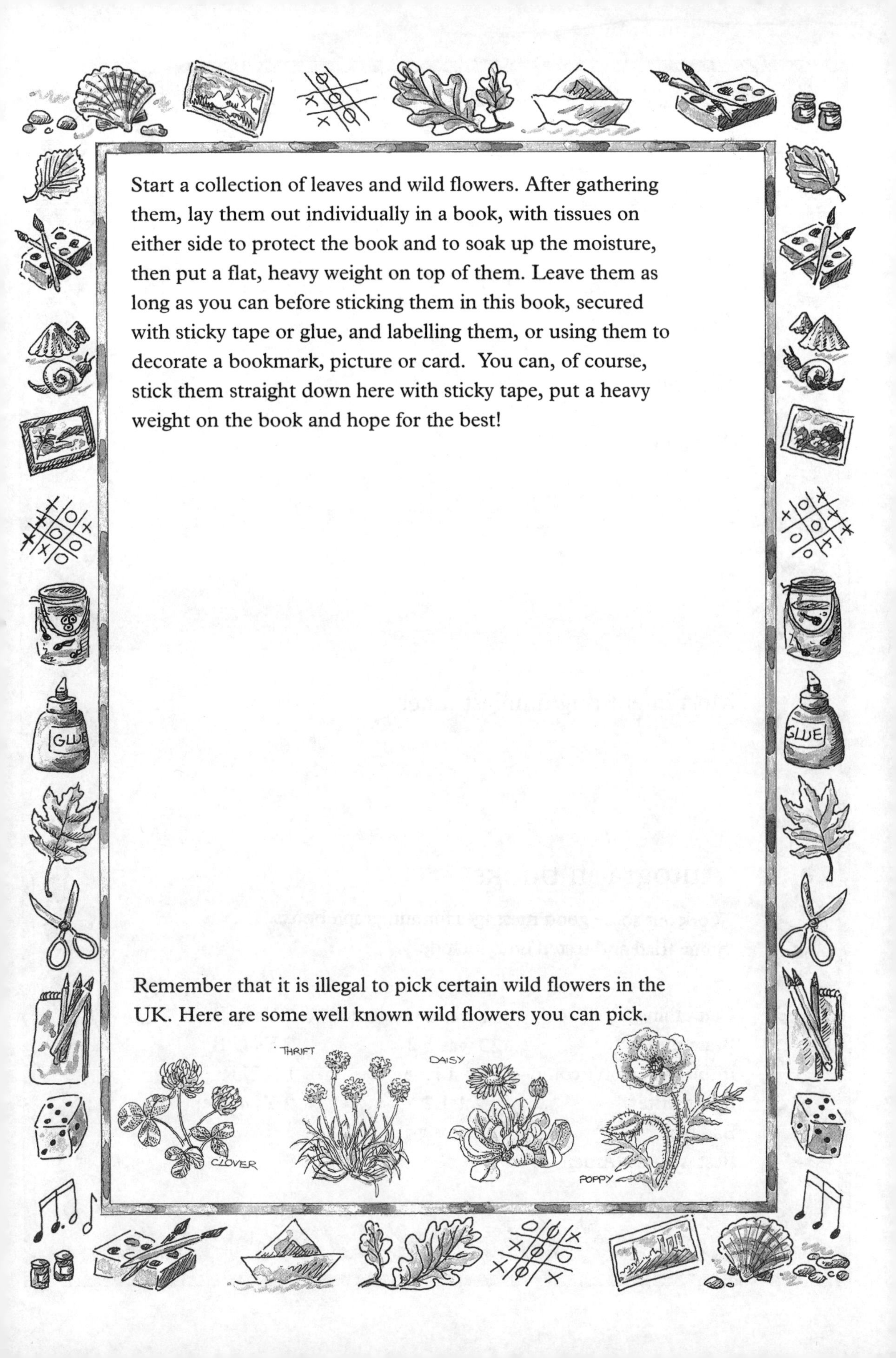

Start a collection of leaves and wild flowers. After gathering them, lay them out individually in a book, with tissues on either side to protect the book and to soak up the moisture, then put a flat, heavy weight on top of them. Leave them as long as you can before sticking them in this book, secured with sticky tape or glue, and labelling them, or using them to decorate a bookmark, picture or card. You can, of course, stick them straight down here with sticky tape, put a heavy weight on the book and hope for the best!

Remember that it is illegal to pick certain wild flowers in the UK. Here are some well known wild flowers you can pick.

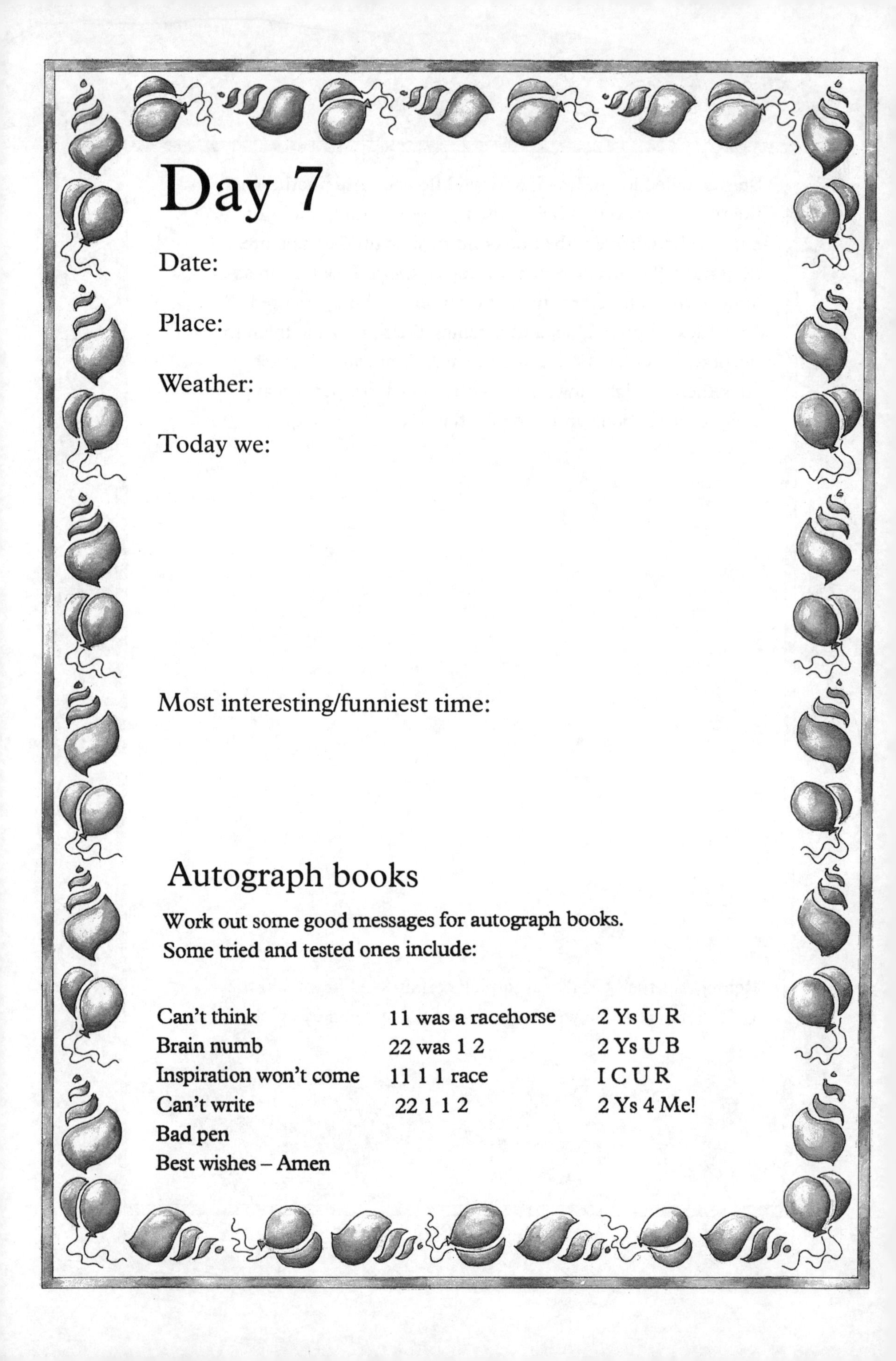

Day 7

Date:

Place:

Weather:

Today we:

Most interesting/funniest time:

Autograph books

Work out some good messages for autograph books.
Some tried and tested ones include:

Can't think
Brain numb
Inspiration won't come
Can't write
Bad pen
Best wishes – Amen

11 was a racehorse
22 was 1 2
11 1 1 race
22 1 1 2

2 Ys U R
2 Ys U B
I C U R
2 Ys 4 Me!

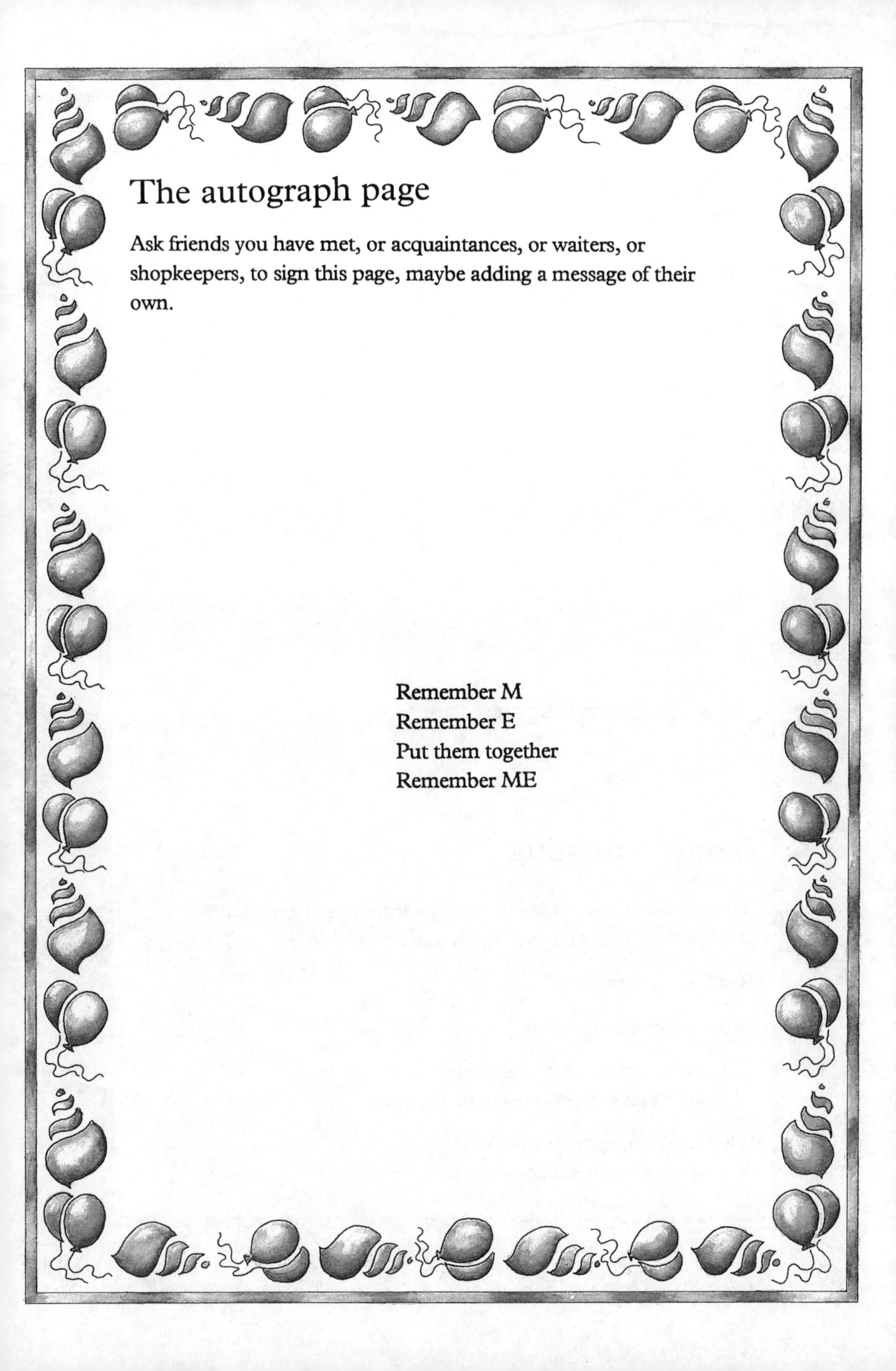

The autograph page

Ask friends you have met, or acquaintances, or waiters, or shopkeepers, to sign this page, maybe adding a message of their own.

Remember M
Remember E
Put them together
Remember ME

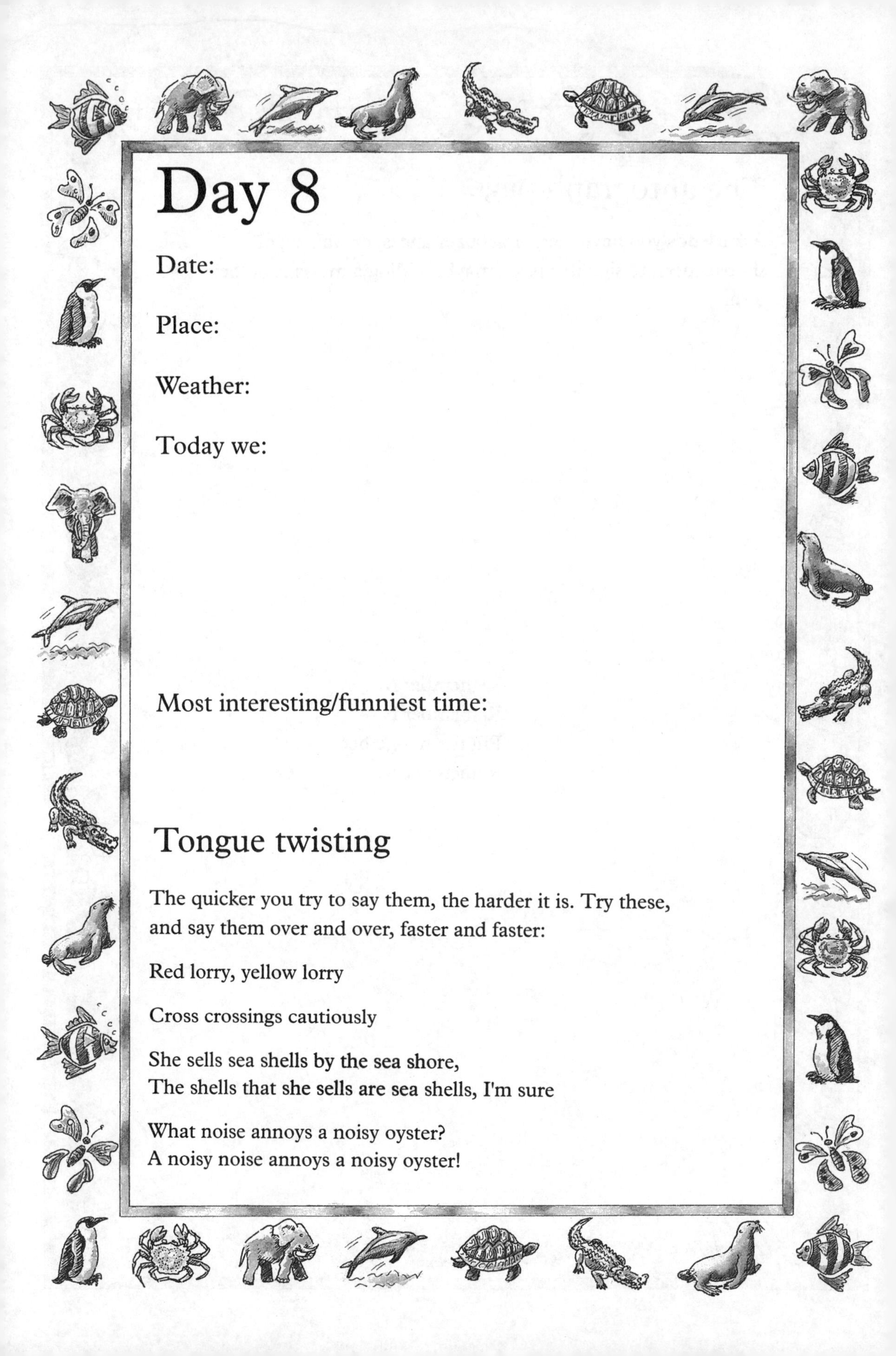

Day 8

Date:

Place:

Weather:

Today we:

Most interesting/funniest time:

Tongue twisting

The quicker you try to say them, the harder it is. Try these, and say them over and over, faster and faster:

Red lorry, yellow lorry

Cross crossings cautiously

She sells sea shells by the sea shore,
The shells that she sells are sea shells, I'm sure

What noise annoys a noisy oyster?
A noisy noise annoys a noisy oyster!

Ask one of your travelling companions to draw another companion. See if it's recognizable.

Round songs

In round songs everyone tries to sing the same tune, at different times, which is not always easy. The first person starts with the first line then continues to the next, at which point the second person starts the first line, and so on.

London's Burning
London's burning, London's burning,
Fetch the engine, fetch the engine,
Fire, fire! Fire, fire!
Pour on water, pour on water.

Frère Jacques
Frère Jacques, Frère Jacques
Dormez-vous? Dormez vous?
Sonnez les matines, sonnez les matines,
Ding, dang, dong, ding, dang, dong.

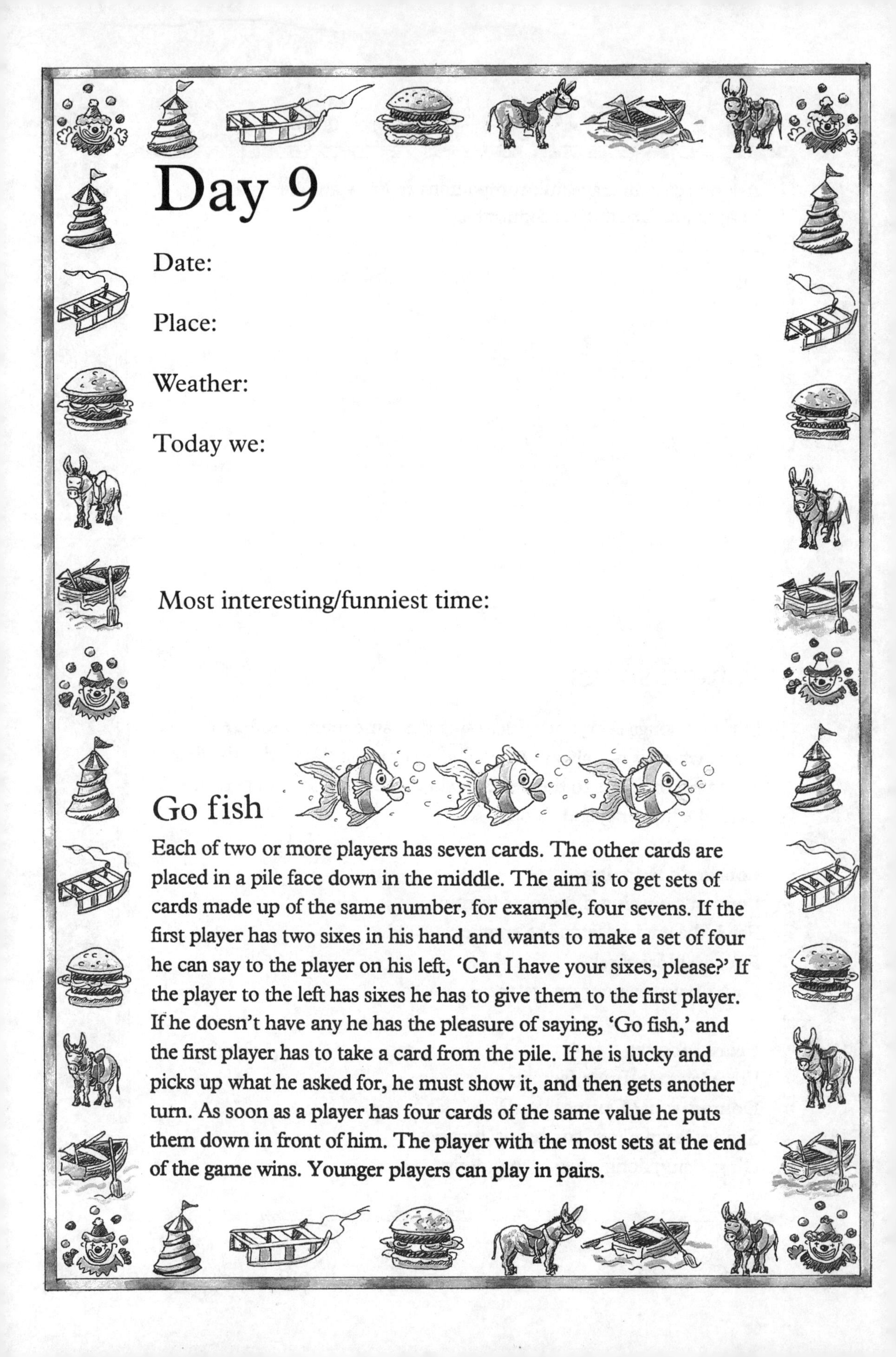

Day 9

Date:

Place:

Weather:

Today we:

Most interesting/funniest time:

Go fish

Each of two or more players has seven cards. The other cards are placed in a pile face down in the middle. The aim is to get sets of cards made up of the same number, for example, four sevens. If the first player has two sixes in his hand and wants to make a set of four he can say to the player on his left, 'Can I have your sixes, please?' If the player to the left has sixes he has to give them to the first player. If he doesn't have any he has the pleasure of saying, 'Go fish,' and the first player has to take a card from the pile. If he is lucky and picks up what he asked for, he must show it, and then gets another turn. As soon as a player has four cards of the same value he puts them down in front of him. The player with the most sets at the end of the game wins. Younger players can play in pairs.

Make up a pattern out of hearts, clubs, spades and diamonds. If you had to make up a fifth card sign, what shape would it be?

Pig

This is a good family game. From a pack of cards take one set (four queens, for instance) for each person playing. Shuffle the sets together and deal the cards so that each person receives four cards. The purpose of the game is to collect a set. Do this by discarding a card to your left and picking up the card the person on your right has discarded. As soon as you have collected your set you must put your finger on your nose – and so must everyone else. The last person to notice the winner's finger on their nose and to copy the action loses – and is Pig. He or she must make a piggy noise, oink, oink!

It's great fun to watch people again and again become so intent on getting sets that they fail to notice the finger on the nose and therefore suffer the embarrassment of becoming Pig. The trick is to watch those noses.

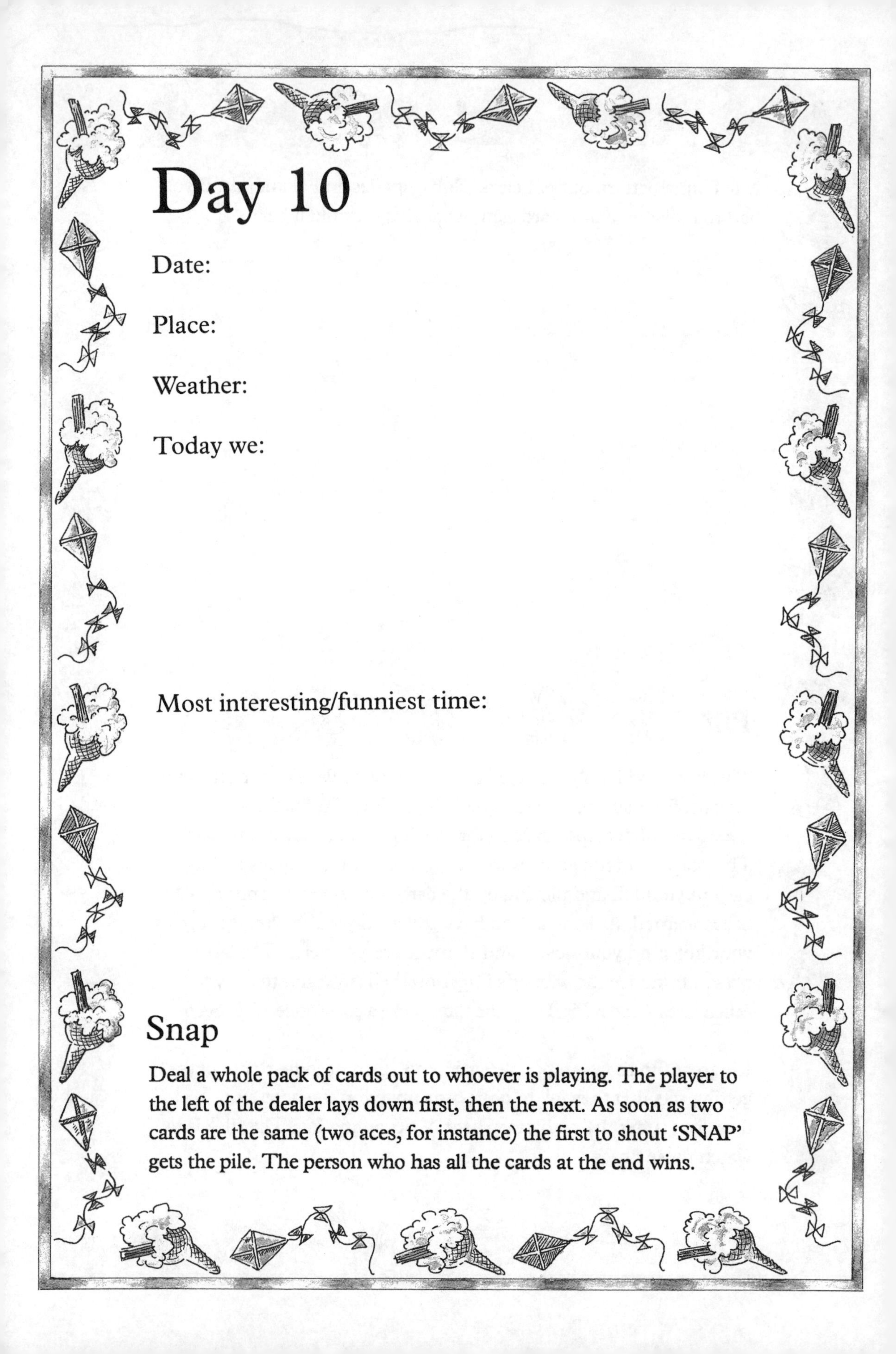

Day 10

Date:

Place:

Weather:

Today we:

Most interesting/funniest time:

Snap

Deal a whole pack of cards out to whoever is playing. The player to the left of the dealer lays down first, then the next. As soon as two cards are the same (two aces, for instance) the first to shout 'SNAP' gets the pile. The person who has all the cards at the end wins.

See if you can draw the best moment of your holiday.

Make a hat

Make a hat from sheets of newspaper or paper, and then decorate it. Will you be Napoleon? Or Nelson?

1. Fold a piece of paper in half

2. Fold top corners over

3. Fold the bottom edge over on each side and press flat

4. Fix both ends with sticky tape and open out to make a hat

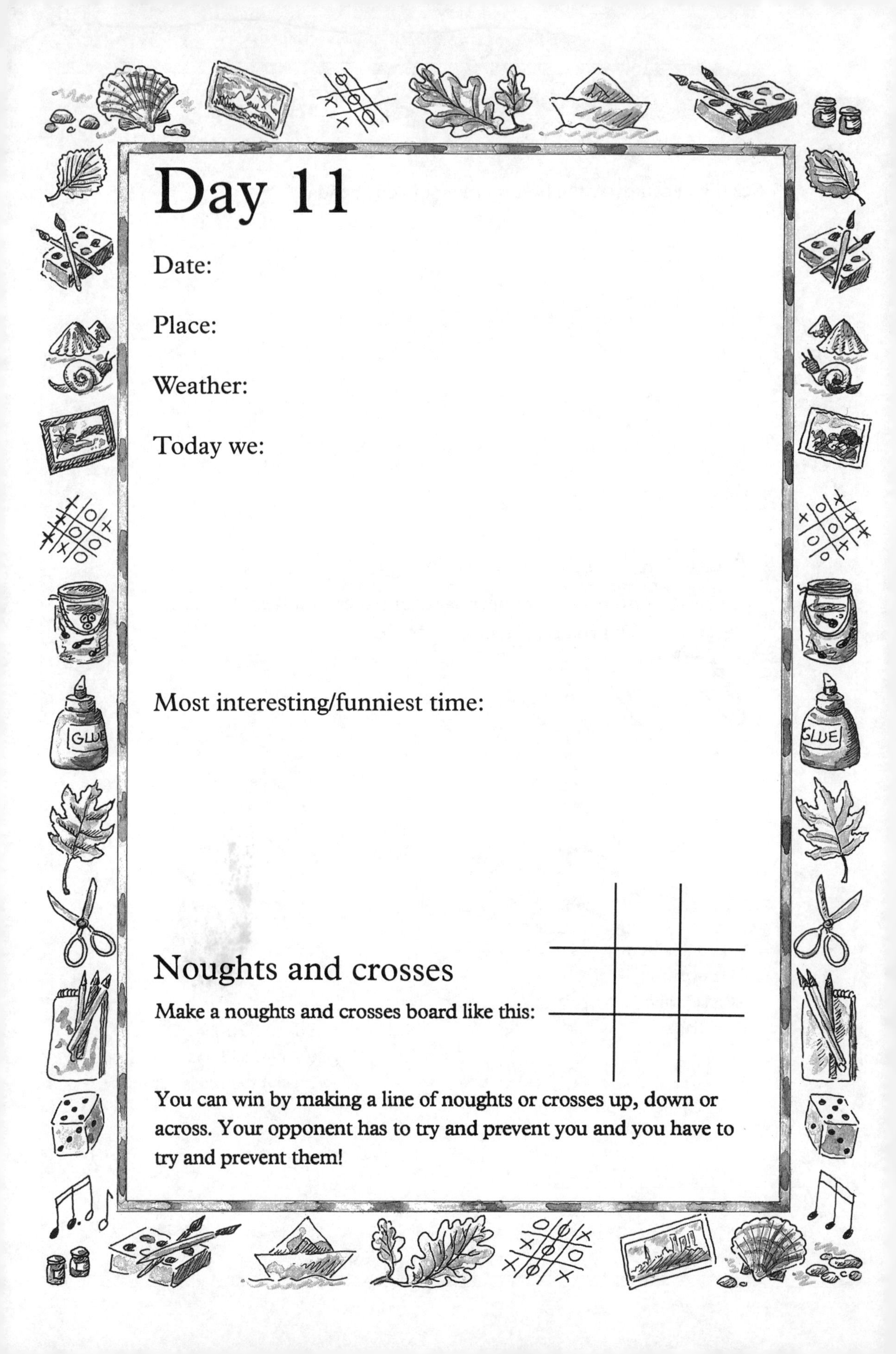

Day 11

Date:

Place:

Weather:

Today we:

Most interesting/funniest time:

Noughts and crosses

Make a noughts and crosses board like this:

You can win by making a line of noughts or crosses up, down or across. Your opponent has to try and prevent you and you have to try and prevent them!

Have a grand tournament!

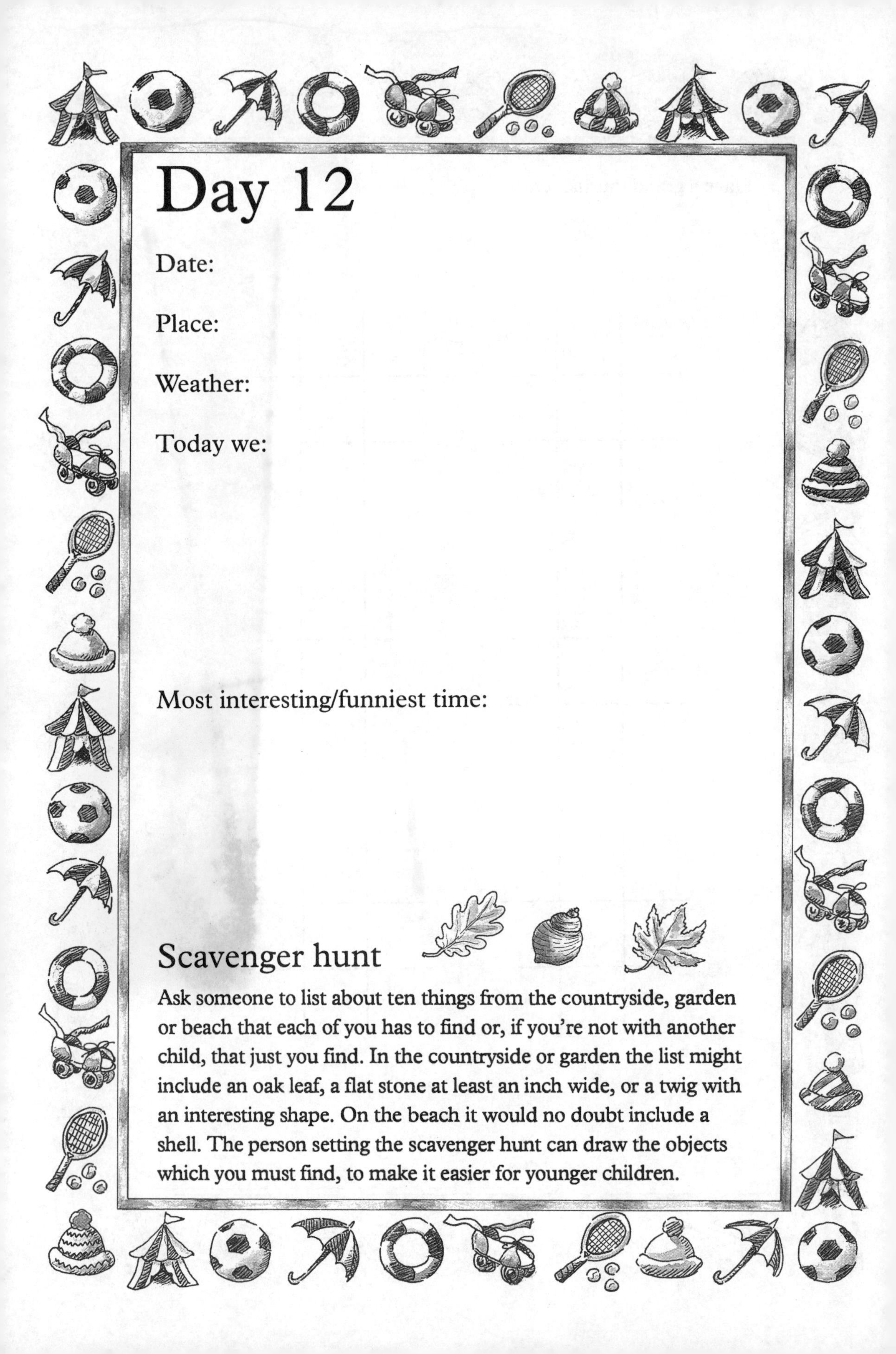

Day 12

Date:

Place:

Weather:

Today we:

Most interesting/funniest time:

Scavenger hunt

Ask someone to list about ten things from the countryside, garden or beach that each of you has to find or, if you're not with another child, that just you find. In the countryside or garden the list might include an oak leaf, a flat stone at least an inch wide, or a twig with an interesting shape. On the beach it would no doubt include a shell. The person setting the scavenger hunt can draw the objects which you must find, to make it easier for younger children.

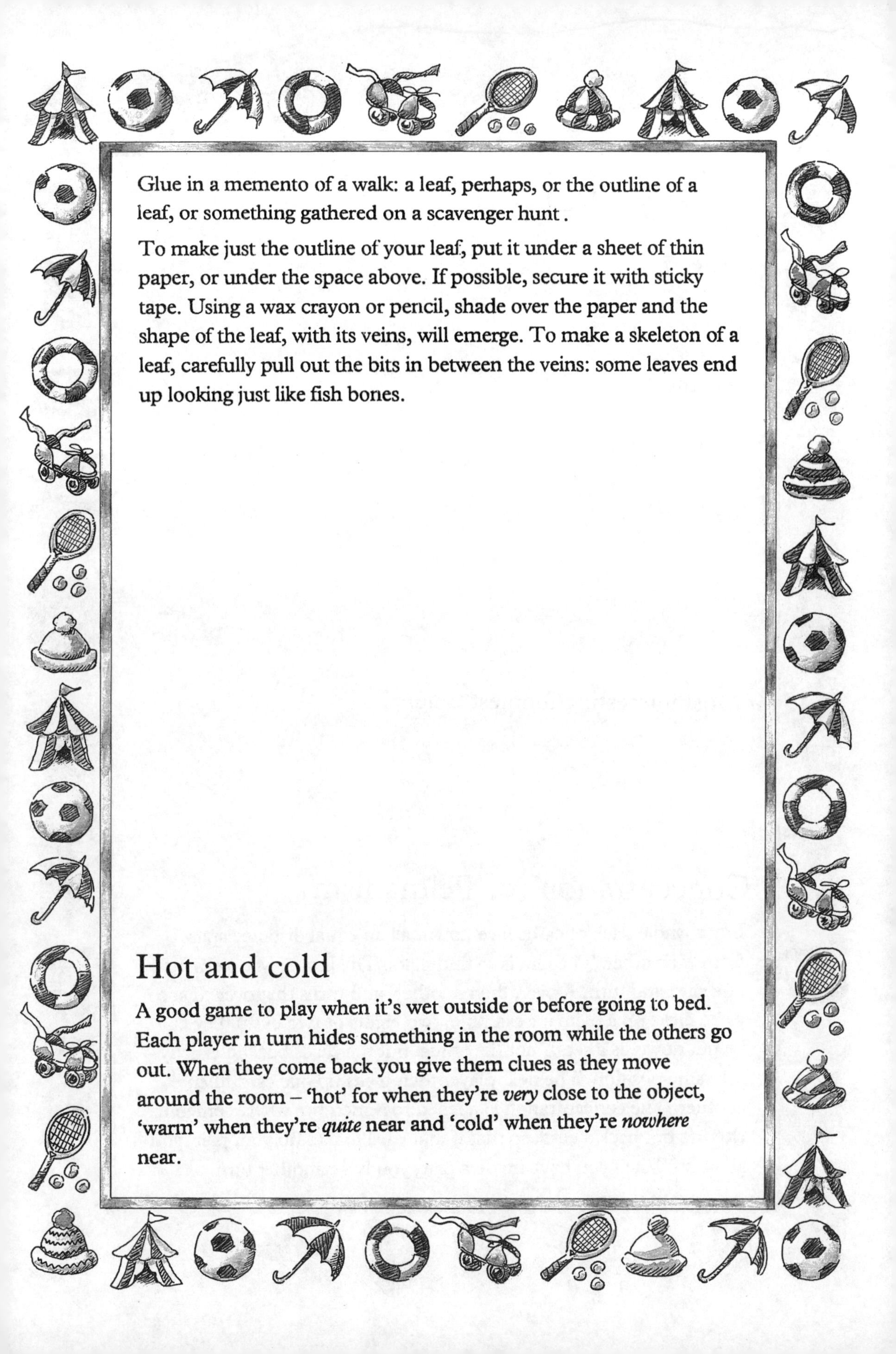

Glue in a memento of a walk: a leaf, perhaps, or the outline of a leaf, or something gathered on a scavenger hunt .

To make just the outline of your leaf, put it under a sheet of thin paper, or under the space above. If possible, secure it with sticky tape. Using a wax crayon or pencil, shade over the paper and the shape of the leaf, with its veins, will emerge. To make a skeleton of a leaf, carefully pull out the bits in between the veins: some leaves end up looking just like fish bones.

Hot and cold

A good game to play when it's wet outside or before going to bed. Each player in turn hides something in the room while the others go out. When they come back you give them clues as they move around the room – 'hot' for when they're *very* close to the object, 'warm' when they're *quite* near and 'cold' when they're *nowhere* near.

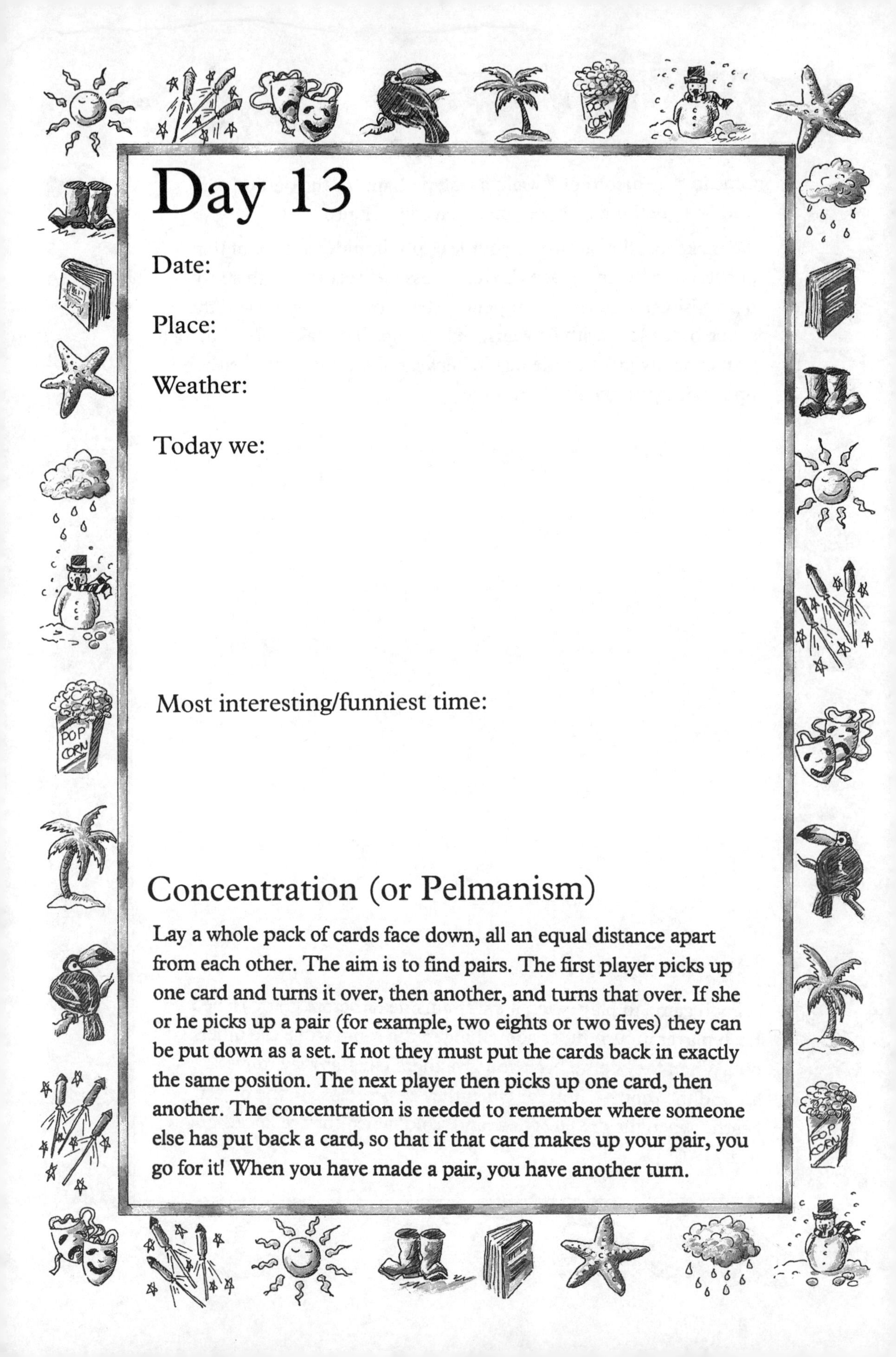

Day 13

Date:

Place:

Weather:

Today we:

Most interesting/funniest time:

Concentration (or Pelmanism)

Lay a whole pack of cards face down, all an equal distance apart from each other. The aim is to find pairs. The first player picks up one card and turns it over, then another, and turns that over. If she or he picks up a pair (for example, two eights or two fives) they can be put down as a set. If not they must put the cards back in exactly the same position. The next player then picks up one card, then another. The concentration is needed to remember where someone else has put back a card, so that if that card makes up your pair, you go for it! When you have made a pair, you have another turn.

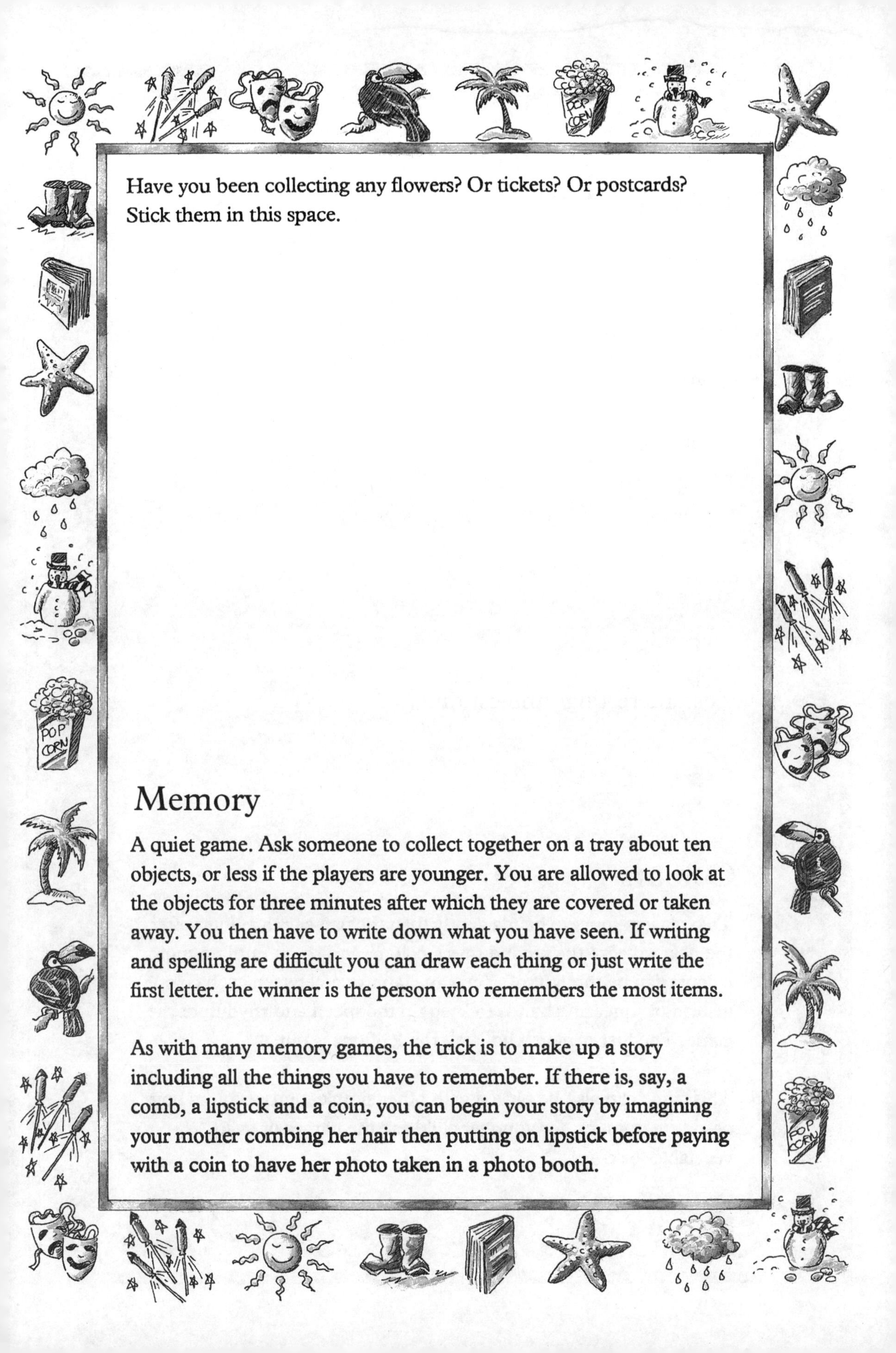

Have you been collecting any flowers? Or tickets? Or postcards? Stick them in this space.

Memory

A quiet game. Ask someone to collect together on a tray about ten objects, or less if the players are younger. You are allowed to look at the objects for three minutes after which they are covered or taken away. You then have to write down what you have seen. If writing and spelling are difficult you can draw each thing or just write the first letter. the winner is the person who remembers the most items.

As with many memory games, the trick is to make up a story including all the things you have to remember. If there is, say, a comb, a lipstick and a coin, you can begin your story by imagining your mother combing her hair then putting on lipstick before paying with a coin to have her photo taken in a photo booth.

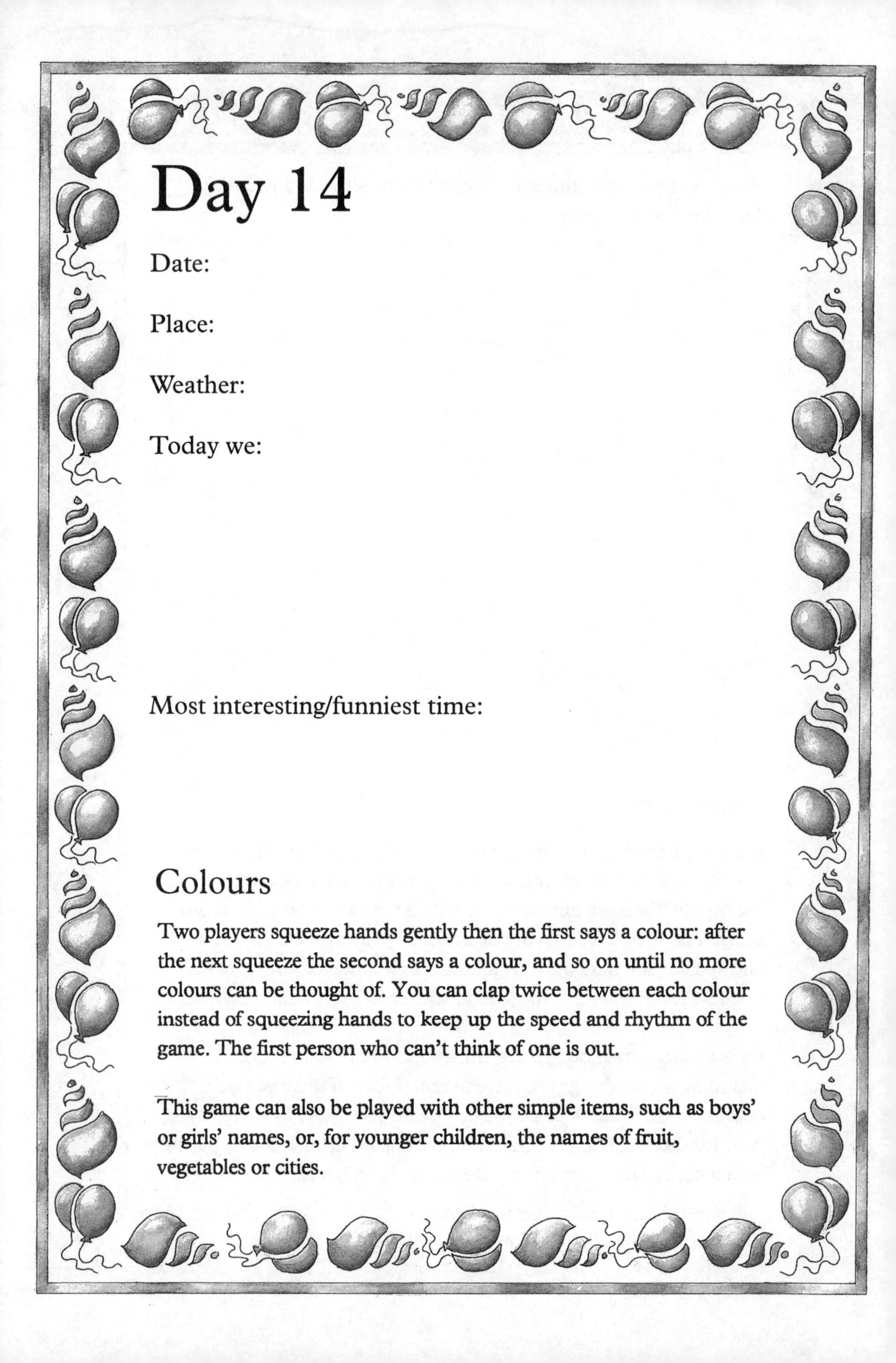

Day 14

Date:

Place:

Weather:

Today we:

Most interesting/funniest time:

Colours

Two players squeeze hands gently then the first says a colour: after the next squeeze the second says a colour, and so on until no more colours can be thought of. You can clap twice between each colour instead of squeezing hands to keep up the speed and rhythm of the game. The first person who can't think of one is out.

This game can also be played with other simple items, such as boys' or girls' names, or, for younger children, the names of fruit, vegetables or cities.

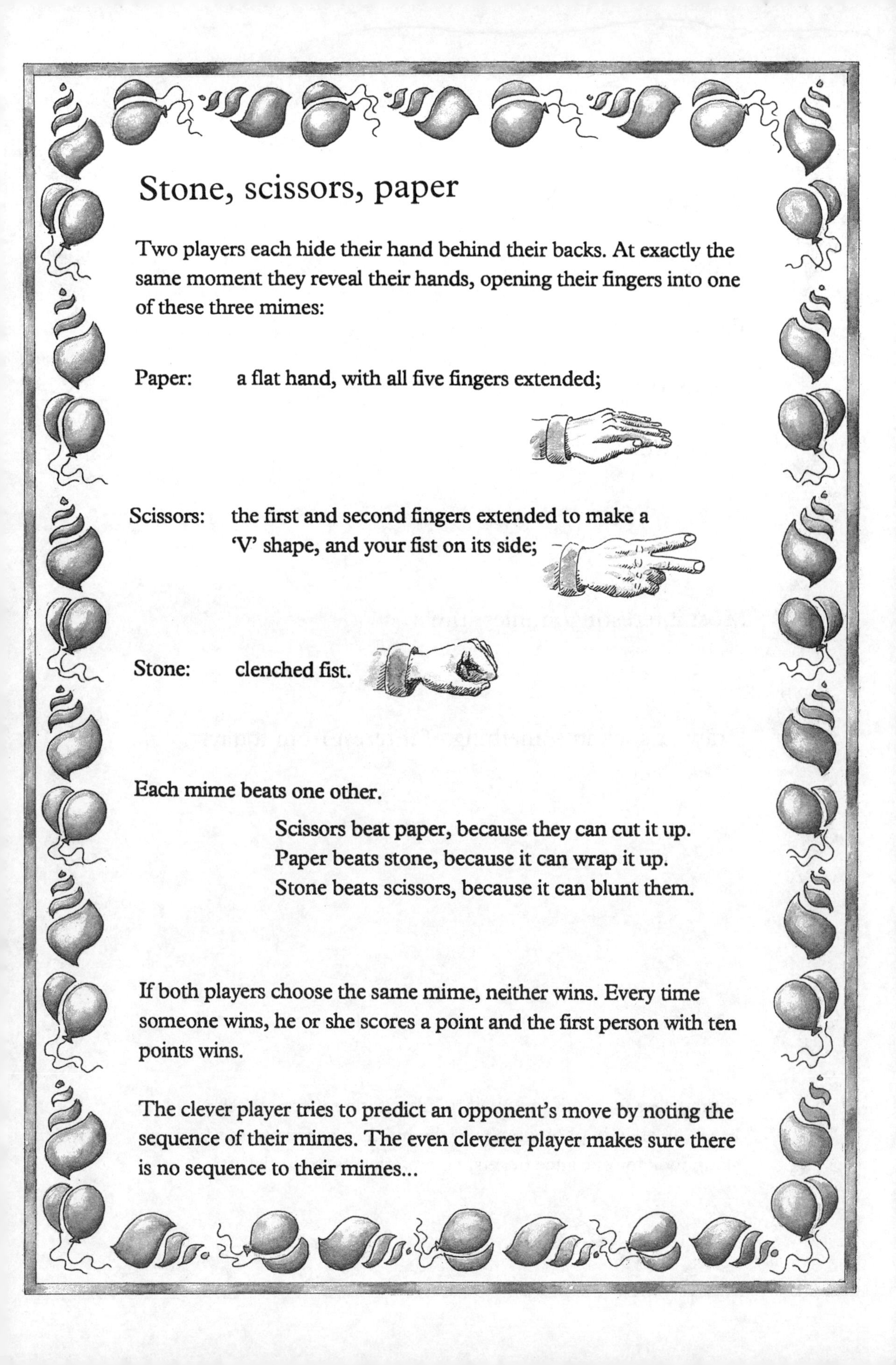

Stone, scissors, paper

Two players each hide their hand behind their backs. At exactly the same moment they reveal their hands, opening their fingers into one of these three mimes:

Paper: a flat hand, with all five fingers extended;

Scissors: the first and second fingers extended to make a 'V' shape, and your fist on its side;

Stone: clenched fist.

Each mime beats one other.

Scissors beat paper, because they can cut it up.
Paper beats stone, because it can wrap it up.
Stone beats scissors, because it can blunt them.

If both players choose the same mime, neither wins. Every time someone wins, he or she scores a point and the first person with ten points wins.

The clever player tries to predict an opponent's move by noting the sequence of their mimes. The even cleverer player makes sure there is no sequence to their mimes...

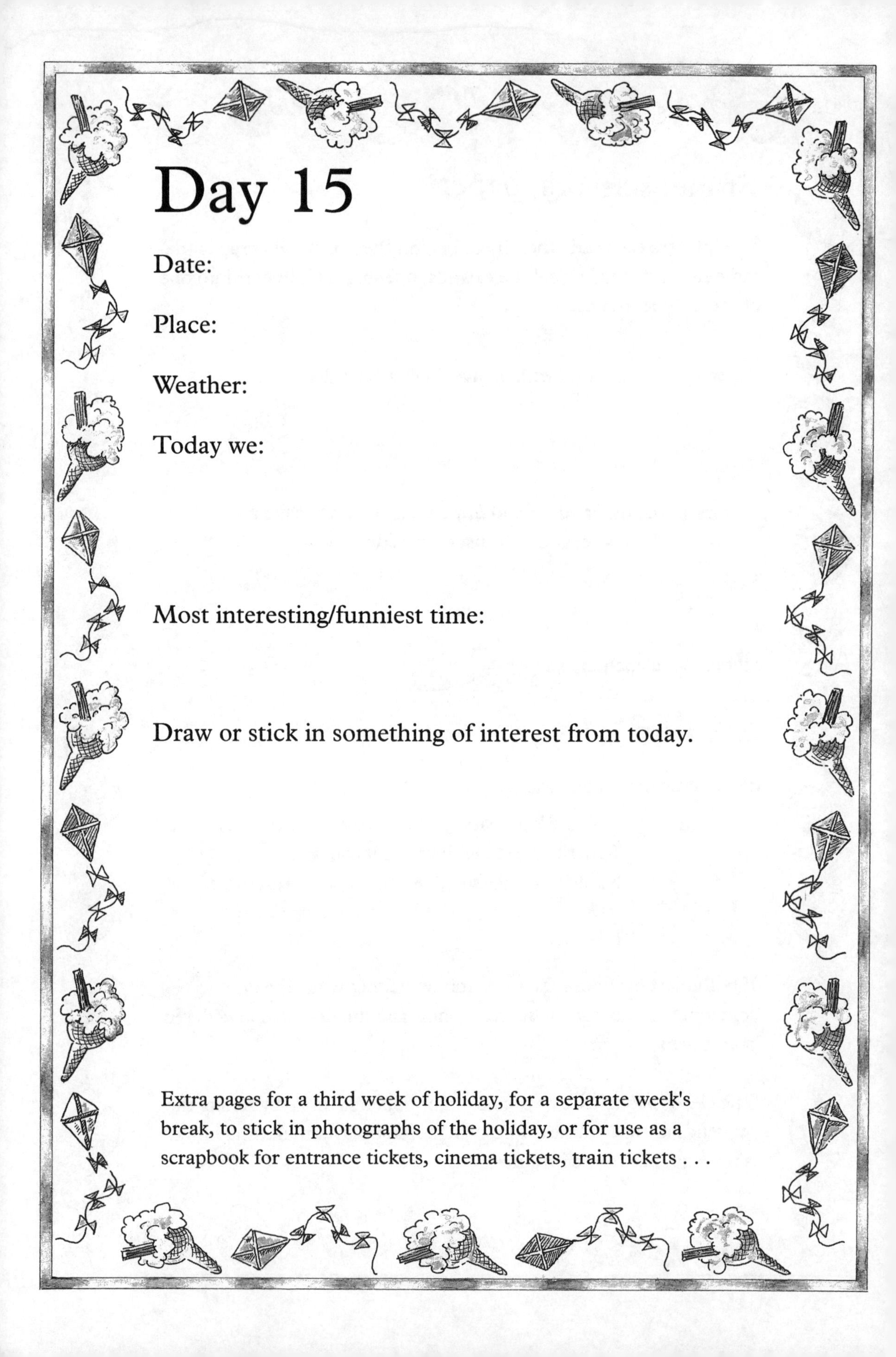

Day 15

Date:

Place:

Weather:

Today we:

Most interesting/funniest time:

Draw or stick in something of interest from today.

Extra pages for a third week of holiday, for a separate week's break, to stick in photographs of the holiday, or for use as a scrapbook for entrance tickets, cinema tickets, train tickets . . .

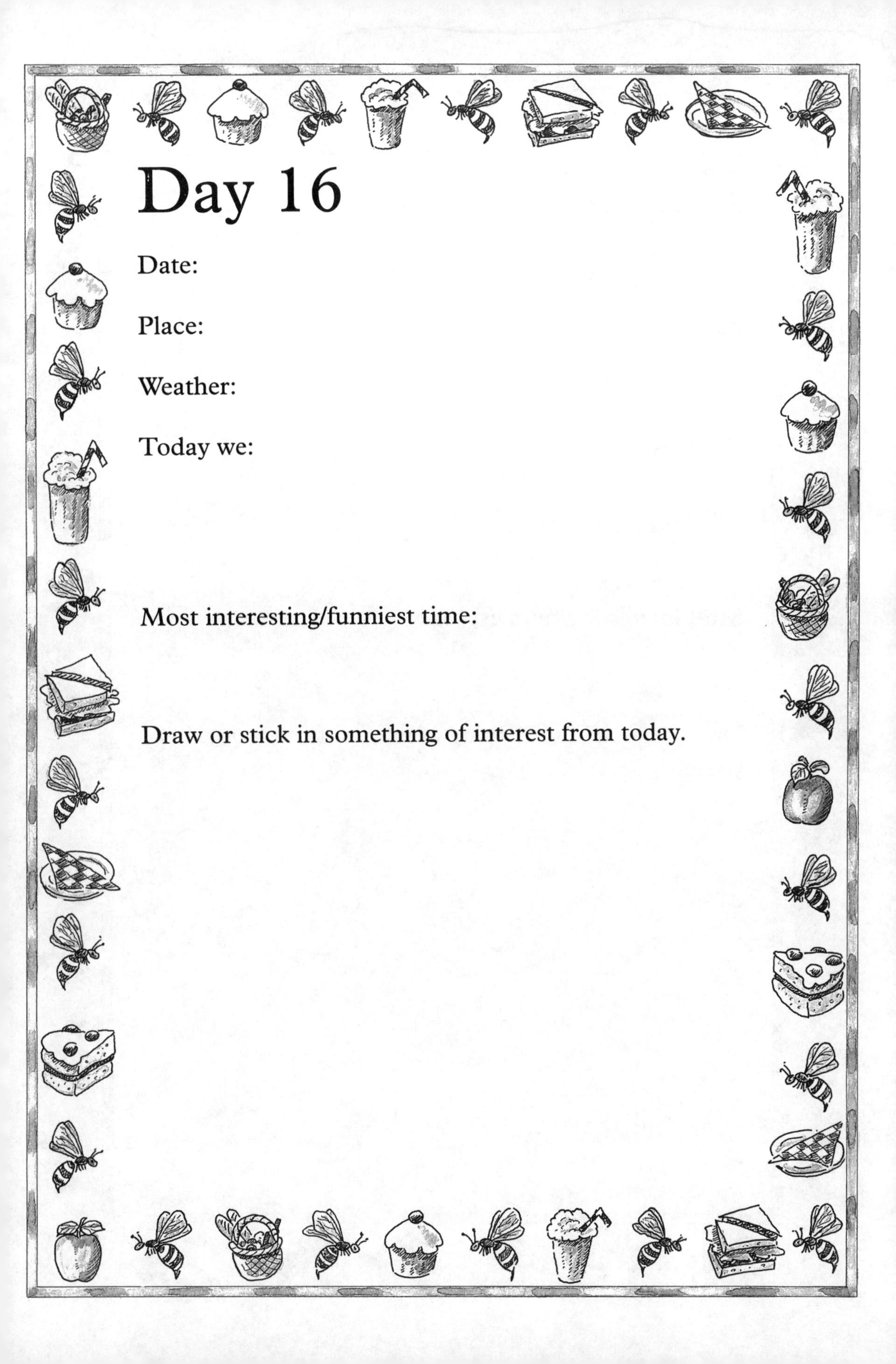

Day 16

Date:

Place:

Weather:

Today we:

Most interesting/funniest time:

Draw or stick in something of interest from today.

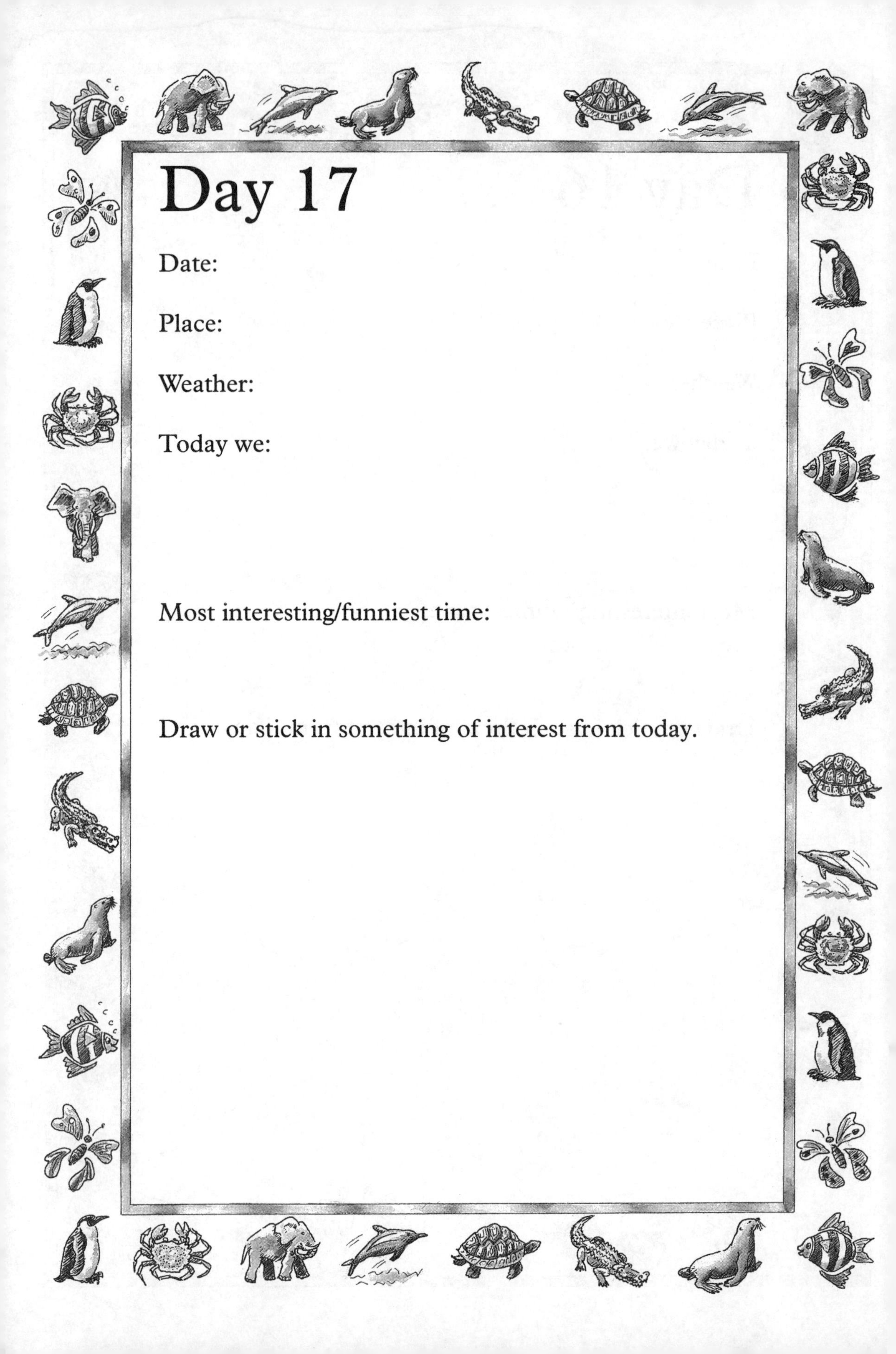

Day 17

Date:

Place:

Weather:

Today we:

Most interesting/funniest time:

Draw or stick in something of interest from today.

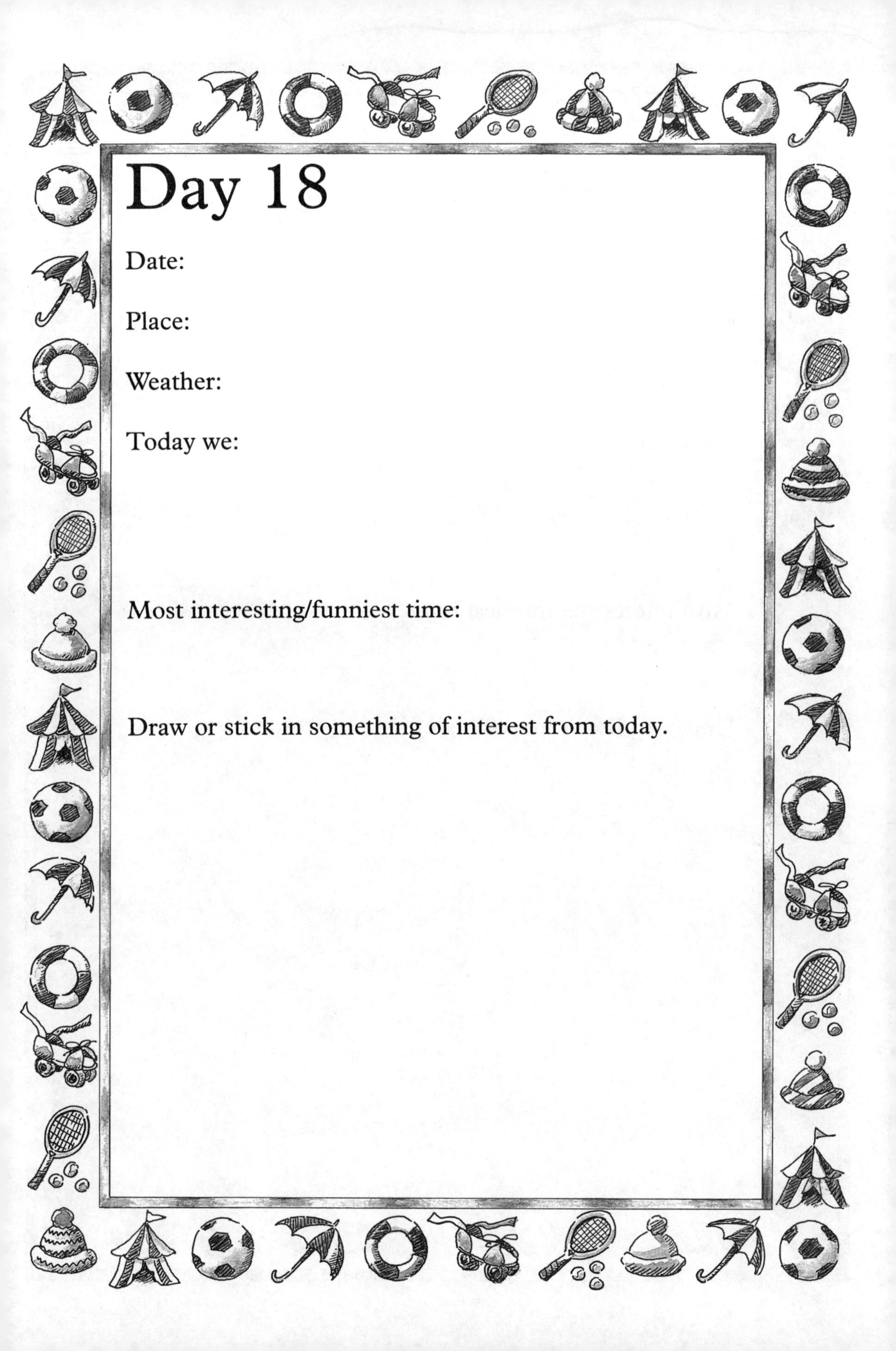

Day 18

Date:

Place:

Weather:

Today we:

Most interesting/funniest time:

Draw or stick in something of interest from today.

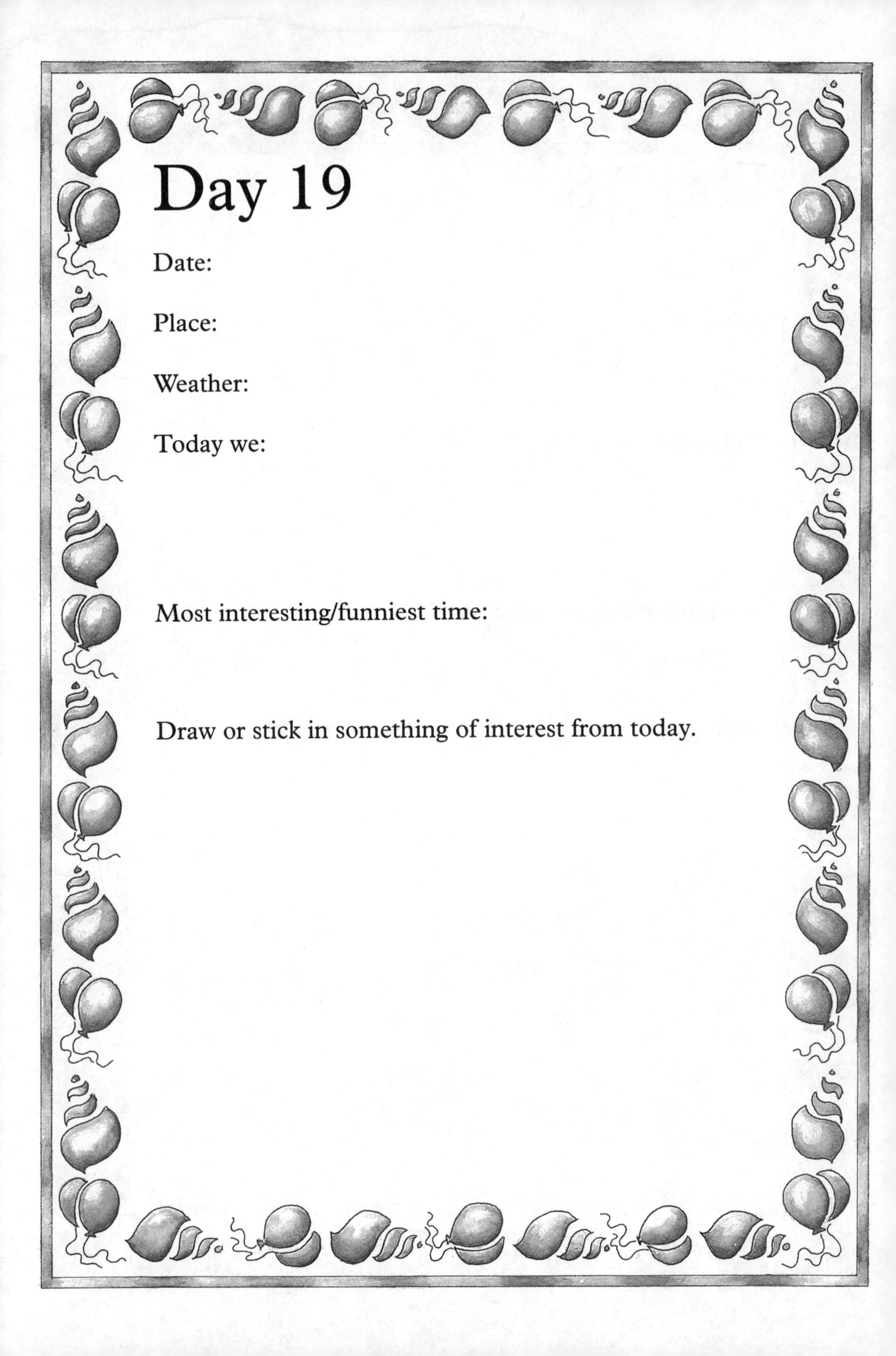

Day 19

Date:

Place:

Weather:

Today we:

Most interesting/funniest time:

Draw or stick in something of interest from today.

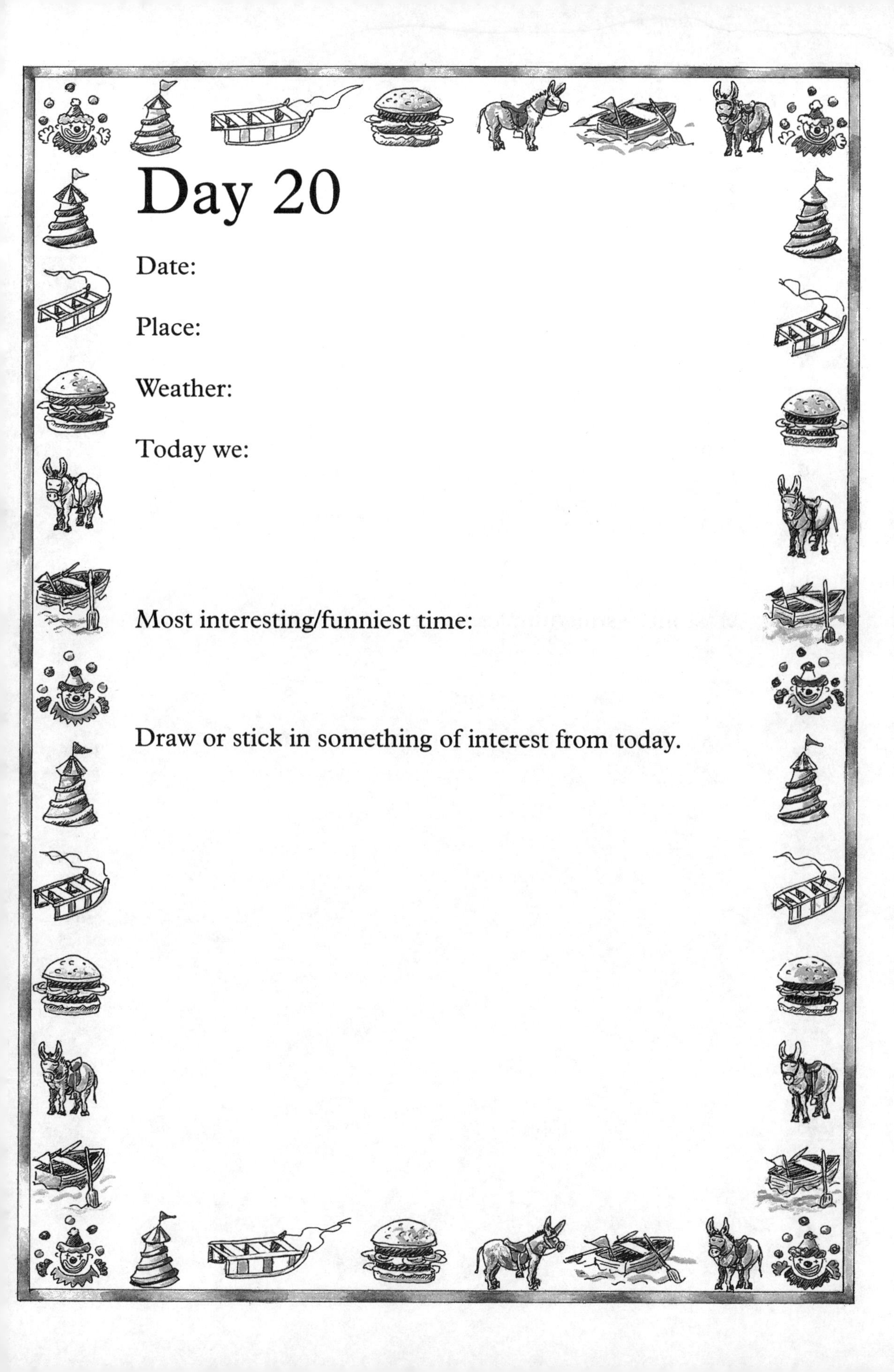

Day 20

Date:

Place:

Weather:

Today we:

Most interesting/funniest time:

Draw or stick in something of interest from today.

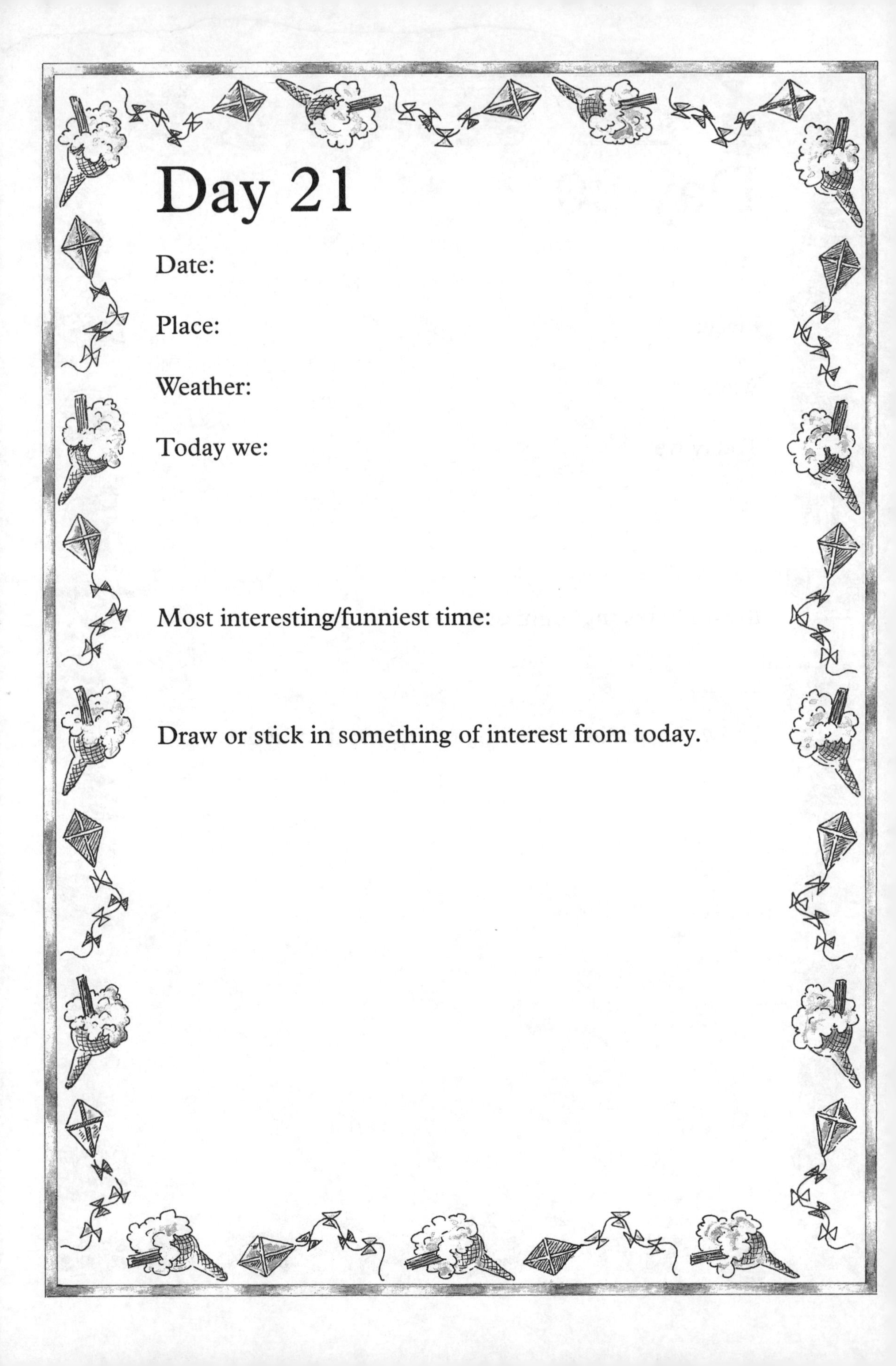

Day 21

Date:

Place:

Weather:

Today we:

Most interesting/funniest time:

Draw or stick in something of interest from today.

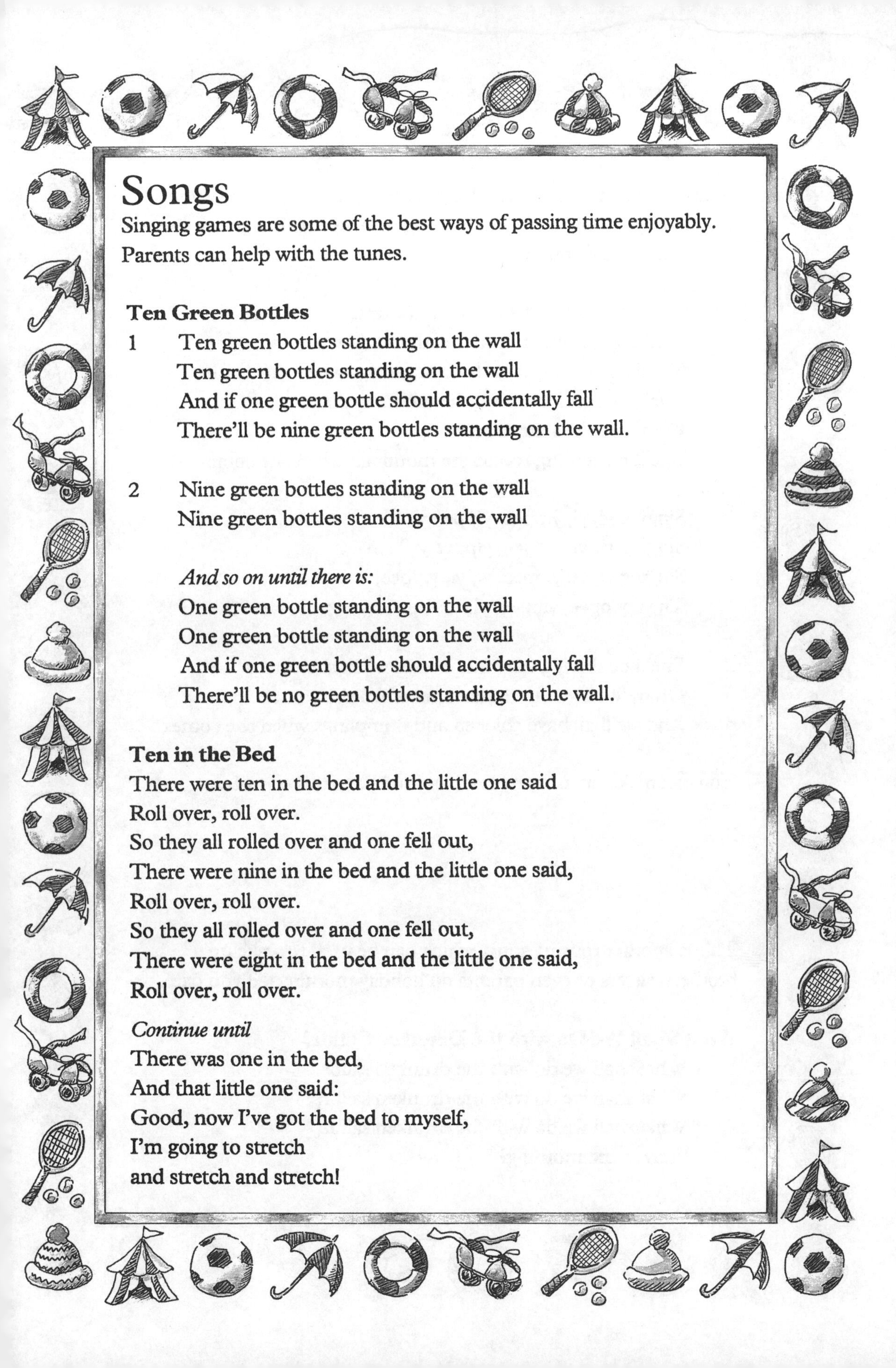

Songs

Singing games are some of the best ways of passing time enjoyably. Parents can help with the tunes.

Ten Green Bottles

1 Ten green bottles standing on the wall
Ten green bottles standing on the wall
And if one green bottle should accidentally fall
There'll be nine green bottles standing on the wall.

2 Nine green bottles standing on the wall
Nine green bottles standing on the wall

And so on until there is:
One green bottle standing on the wall
One green bottle standing on the wall
And if one green bottle should accidentally fall
There'll be no green bottles standing on the wall.

Ten in the Bed

There were ten in the bed and the little one said
Roll over, roll over.
So they all rolled over and one fell out,
There were nine in the bed and the little one said,
Roll over, roll over.
So they all rolled over and one fell out,
There were eight in the bed and the little one said,
Roll over, roll over.

Continue until
There was one in the bed,
And that little one said:
Good, now I've got the bed to myself,
I'm going to stretch
and stretch and stretch!

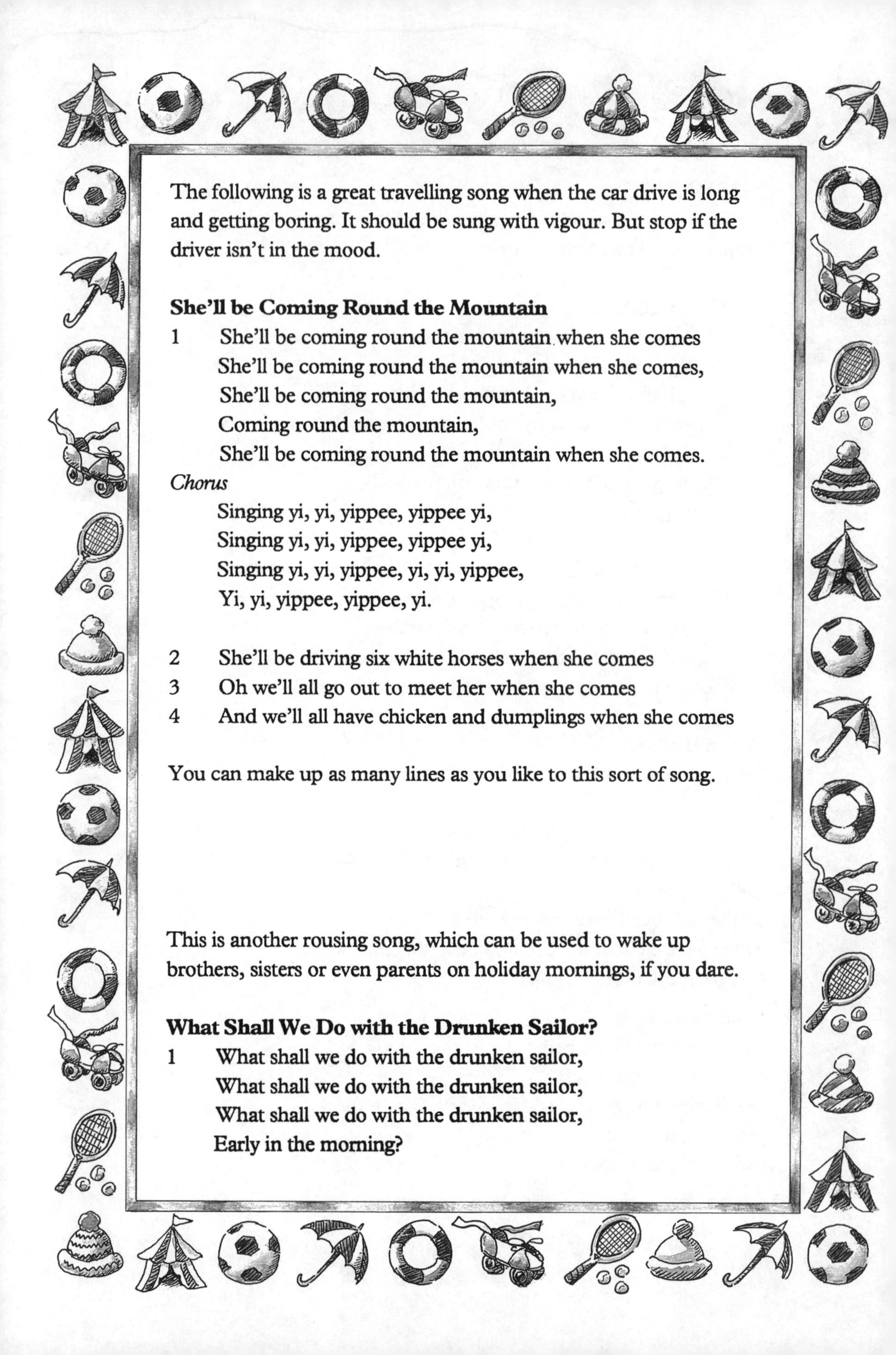

The following is a great travelling song when the car drive is long and getting boring. It should be sung with vigour. But stop if the driver isn't in the mood.

She'll be Coming Round the Mountain

1 She'll be coming round the mountain when she comes
She'll be coming round the mountain when she comes,
She'll be coming round the mountain,
Coming round the mountain,
She'll be coming round the mountain when she comes.

Chorus

Singing yi, yi, yippee, yippee yi,
Singing yi, yi, yippee, yippee yi,
Singing yi, yi, yippee, yi, yi, yippee,
Yi, yi, yippee, yippee, yi.

2 She'll be driving six white horses when she comes
3 Oh we'll all go out to meet her when she comes
4 And we'll all have chicken and dumplings when she comes

You can make up as many lines as you like to this sort of song.

This is another rousing song, which can be used to wake up brothers, sisters or even parents on holiday mornings, if you dare.

What Shall We Do with the Drunken Sailor?

1 What shall we do with the drunken sailor,
What shall we do with the drunken sailor,
What shall we do with the drunken sailor,
Early in the morning?

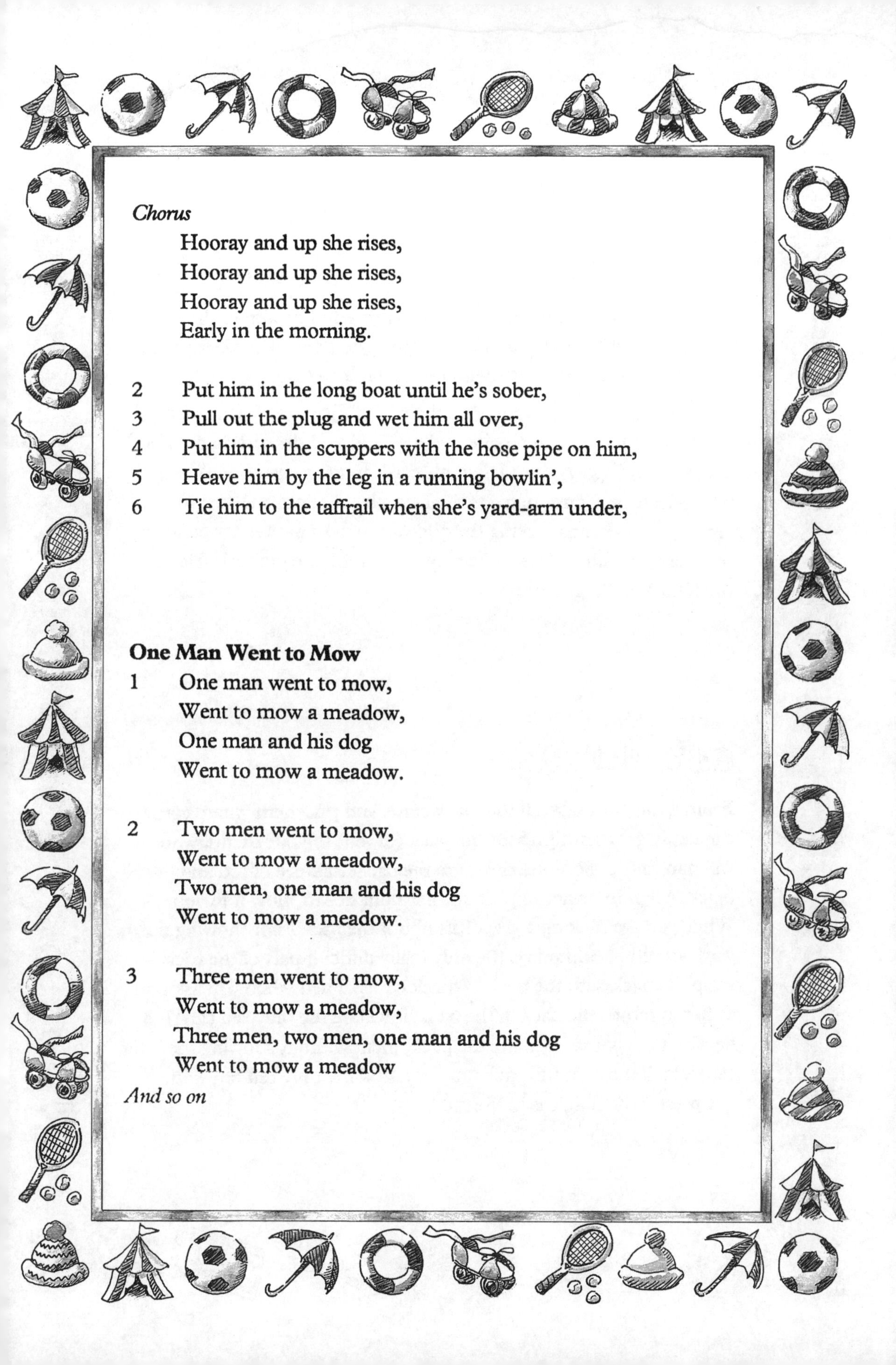

Chorus

Hooray and up she rises,
Hooray and up she rises,
Hooray and up she rises,
Early in the morning.

2 Put him in the long boat until he's sober,
3 Pull out the plug and wet him all over,
4 Put him in the scuppers with the hose pipe on him,
5 Heave him by the leg in a running bowlin',
6 Tie him to the taffrail when she's yard-arm under,

One Man Went to Mow

1 One man went to mow,
Went to mow a meadow,
One man and his dog
Went to mow a meadow.

2 Two men went to mow,
Went to mow a meadow,
Two men, one man and his dog
Went to mow a meadow.

3 Three men went to mow,
Went to mow a meadow,
Three men, two men, one man and his dog
Went to mow a meadow

And so on

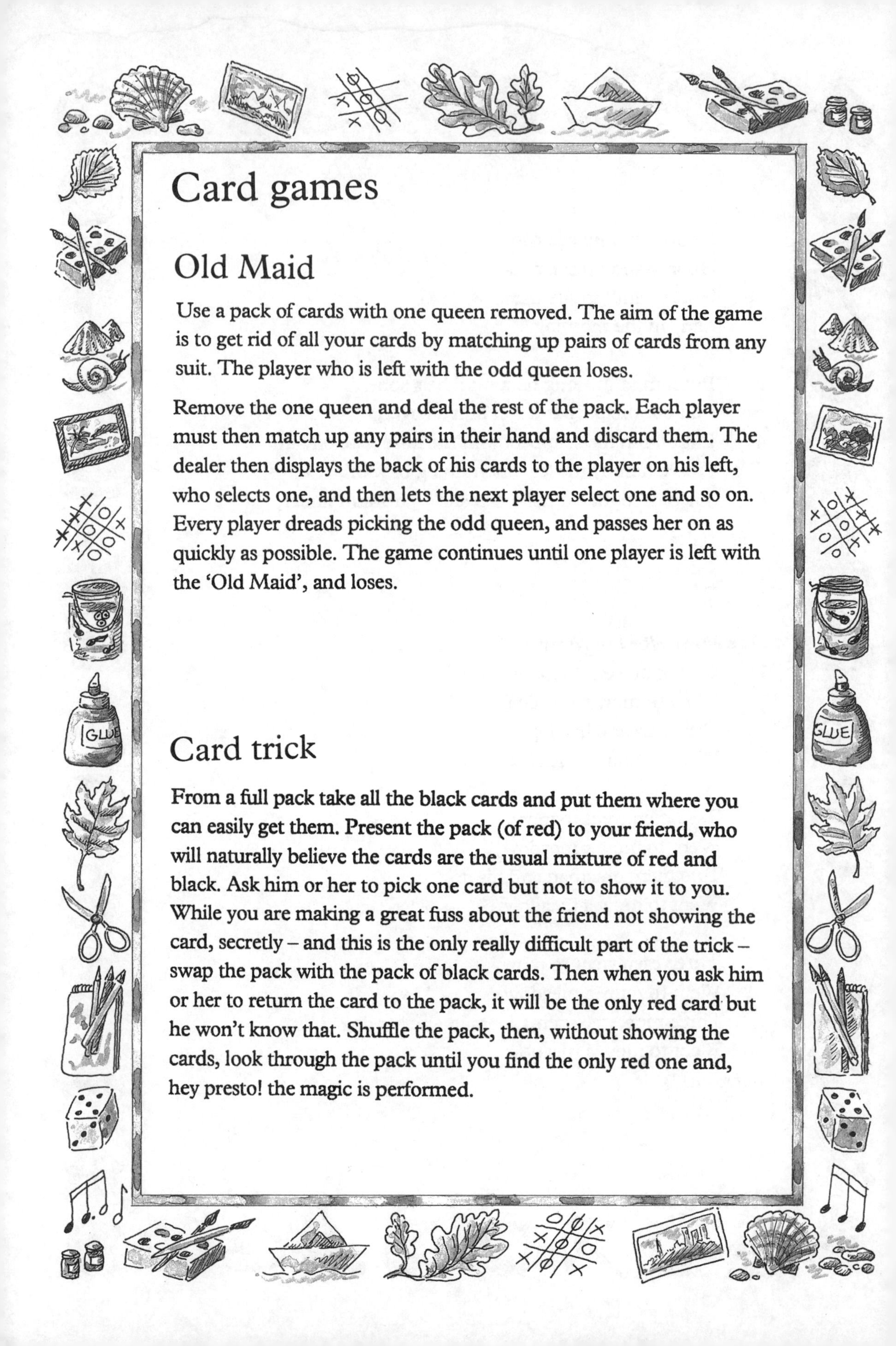

Card games

Old Maid

Use a pack of cards with one queen removed. The aim of the game is to get rid of all your cards by matching up pairs of cards from any suit. The player who is left with the odd queen loses.

Remove the one queen and deal the rest of the pack. Each player must then match up any pairs in their hand and discard them. The dealer then displays the back of his cards to the player on his left, who selects one, and then lets the next player select one and so on. Every player dreads picking the odd queen, and passes her on as quickly as possible. The game continues until one player is left with the 'Old Maid', and loses.

Card trick

From a full pack take all the black cards and put them where you can easily get them. Present the pack (of red) to your friend, who will naturally believe the cards are the usual mixture of red and black. Ask him or her to pick one card but not to show it to you. While you are making a great fuss about the friend not showing the card, secretly – and this is the only really difficult part of the trick – swap the pack with the pack of black cards. Then when you ask him or her to return the card to the pack, it will be the only red card but he won't know that. Shuffle the pack, then, without showing the cards, look through the pack until you find the only red one and, hey presto! the magic is performed.

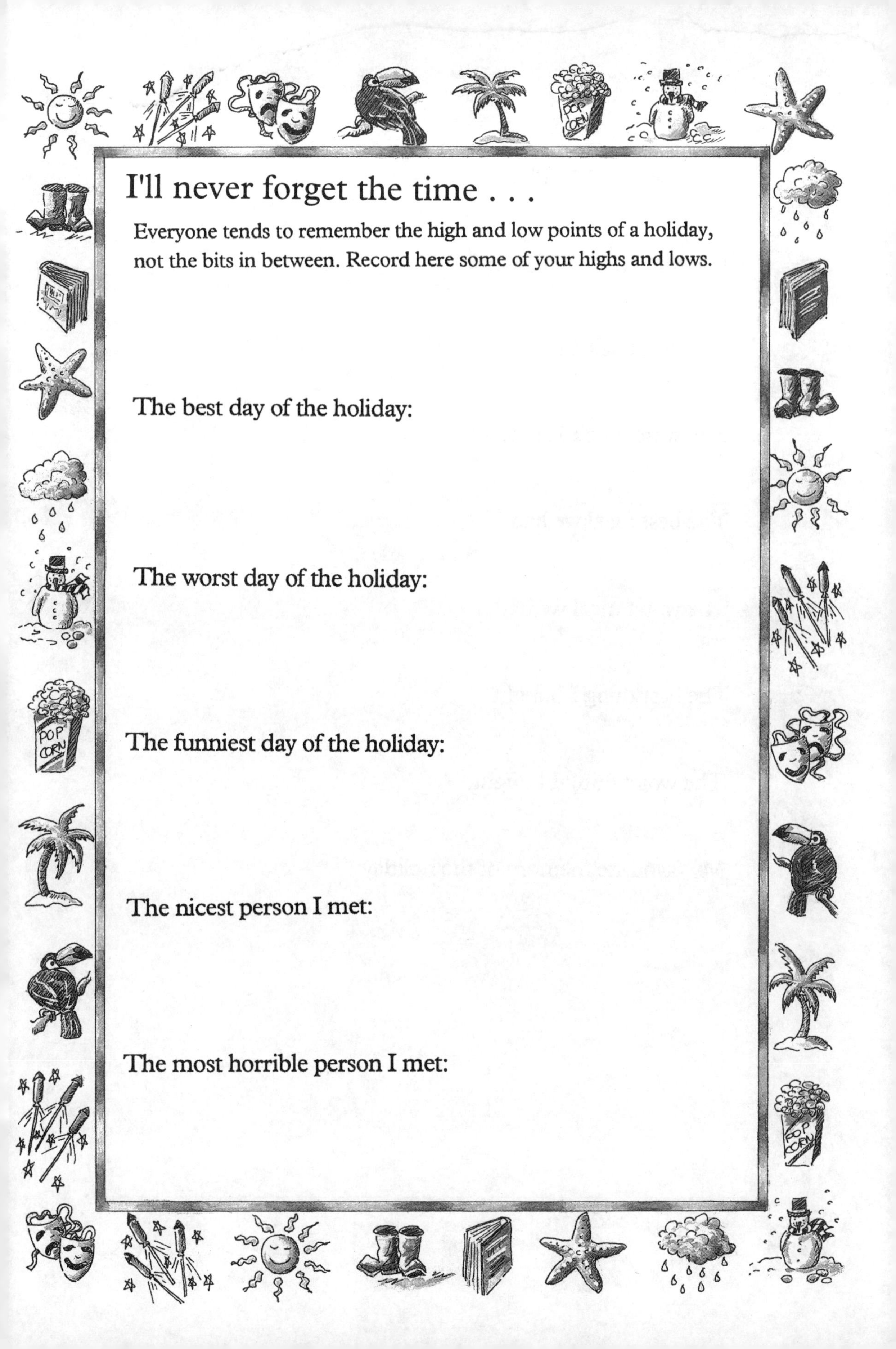

I'll never forget the time . . .

Everyone tends to remember the high and low points of a holiday, not the bits in between. Record here some of your highs and lows.

The best day of the holiday:

The worst day of the holiday:

The funniest day of the holiday:

The nicest person I met:

The most horrible person I met:

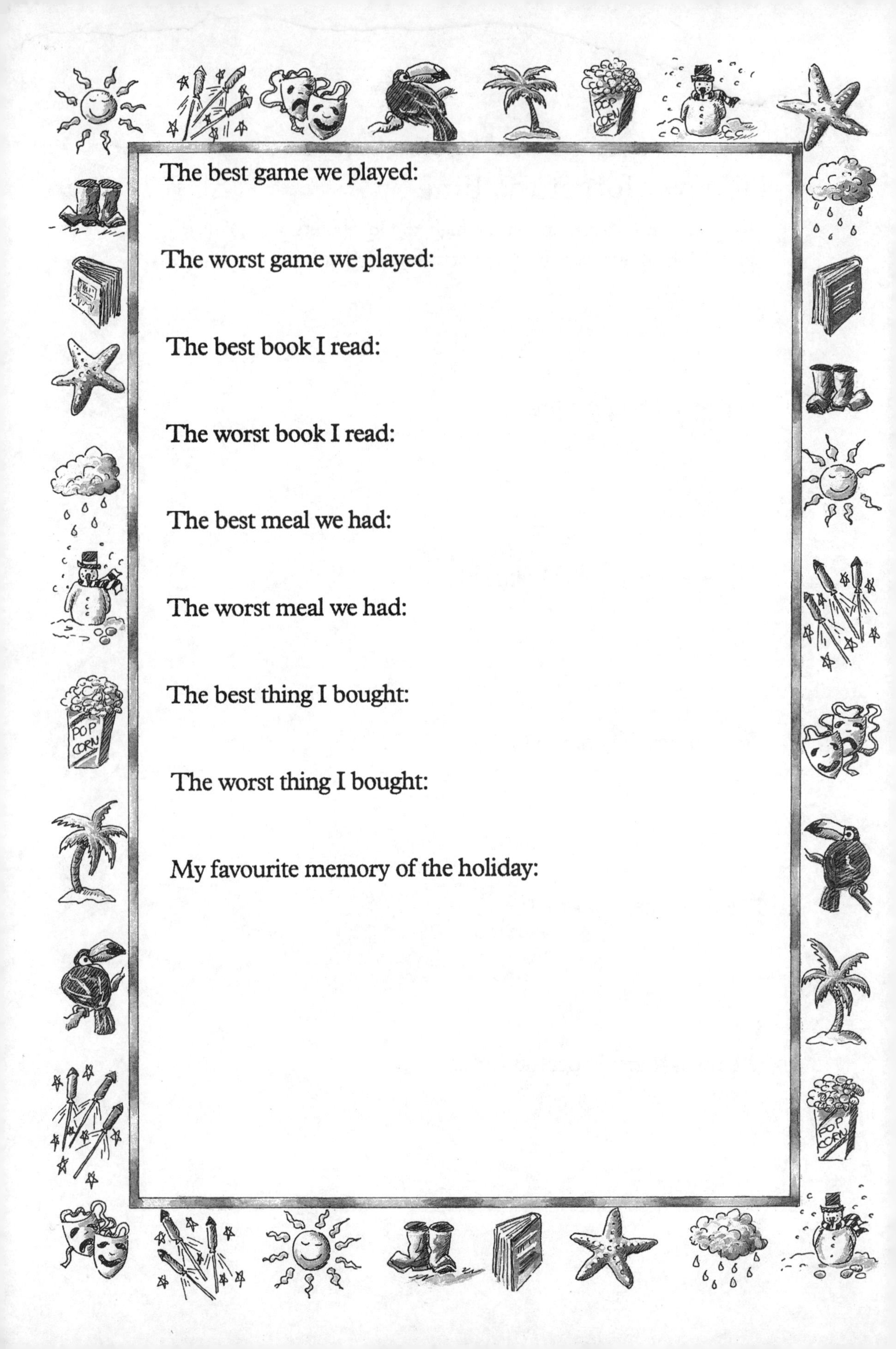

The best game we played:

The worst game we played:

The best book I read:

The worst book I read:

The best meal we had:

The worst meal we had:

The best thing I bought:

The worst thing I bought:

My favourite memory of the holiday: